C   5

M
CANDY

Candy, Edward.
  Bones of contention / Edward Candy.
-- Garden City, N.Y. : Published for
the Crime Club by Doubleday, 1983,
c1954.
  178 p. ; 22 cm.

  ISBN 0-385-18804-8 : $11.95

  I. Title.

CL ME
D000465
          830814
          VAB/VAB
830808 CP1hC
C*   83-B6194
82-45964

Bones of Contention

By Edward Candy

Bones
of Contention

EDWARD CANDY

PUBLISHED FOR THE CRIME CLUB BY
DOUBLEDAY & COMPANY, INC.
GARDEN CITY, NEW YORK
1983

All the characters in this book
are fictitious, and any resemblance
to actual persons, living or dead,
is purely coincidental.

Library of Congress Cataloging in Publication Data

Candy, Edward.
Bones of contention.

I. Title.
PR6064.E83B6   1983   823'.914
ISBN 0-385-18804-8
Library of Congress Catalog Card Number 82–45964

For Prue

"They have got some remarkably fine skeletons lately at the College . . ." says Mr. Candy, across the table, in a loud cheerful voice. "I strongly recommend the Professor, ma'am, when he next has an hour to spare, to pay them a visit."

Wilkie Collins, *The Moonstone*

Bones of Contention

I

There are persons who experience a sense of oppression in the presence of a skeleton. Mr. Murivance was not one of these. "Scott!" he called to a young man who was passing the museum door, "can you spare me a precious moment?"

"I can spare you several moments; they are not so precious." Hilary Scott came into the museum and stood before the skeleton. He was oppressed but did not show it, and in any case it was Mr. Murivance who oppressed him and not the skeleton. "Is this your newest treasure?"

"I have just this moment opened the package. Isn't she beautiful?"

"I suppose so. That is, I suppose it is a she; I will take your word for it. And I suppose she may have been beautiful, but that is too bleak a thought for a November morning. Or perhaps it is exactly the right thought."

Mr. Murivance was not listening. People seldom listened to Hilary when he talked in this way, though he believed his conversation was his principal charm, and would not have been so charming if he had understood his assets a little more clearly.

"She was quite young," Mr. Murivance said. "Adolescent merely, to judge by the state of fusion of the upper humeral epiphyses. But too old for us, nevertheless. She will not be able to stay here."

"Won't she? It seems a pity, when she has only just arrived. Couldn't a point be stretched in her favour?"

"Several points would have to be stretched. Not only is she too old, but she is perfectly normal in every way, so that to include her in a museum of pathological conditions in childhood would be a double solecism. Professor Honeychurch would consider it the thin end of the wedge."

"Where did she come from? Was she a bequest or a loan or merely somebody's unwanted guilty secret?"

"Well, there you have it, Scott. You have got to the heart of the matter at once. I rather fancy she has been sent to the wrong address. Her immediate point of departure was St. Pancras, and there is no letter of explanation with her to make it possible to trace the giver."

"There will be," Hilary said with a sense of administering comfort to the older man. "People do not send skeletons to other people without mentioning the fact. Their intentions might so easily be misunderstood."

Mr. Murivance snickered; the snicker did service for a laugh and was less extravagant of effort. "Certainly," he said, "her mode of transport was equivocal."

Hilary looked across the museum. Among the glass cases stood a cabin trunk.

"Did she come in that?"

"She did. Hardly a fitting conveyance, though one well established, I believe, for corpses in a rather fresher state of preservation." Mr. Murivance snickered again, to underline the breadth of his outlook. "She was addressed to me by name."

"That hardly bears out your assumption of a mistake. Murivance is not a name that one comes across every day. That is, we do come across it every day, but there are others less fortunate."

Mr. Murivance appeared to take credit for the uncommonness of his patronymic, though his existence diminished the quality. He was a thin, delicate-looking man of nearly seventy, with a sharp nose and a habit of peering about as if he were shortsighted, though his sight in fact was excellent; the peering was taken by his colleagues to be symbolic, for his inquisitiveness was a recurrent cause for both laughter and irritation. He had been a good though not outstanding surgeon, who had sworn like many others never to work in a National Health Service; and unlike many others had kept his oath without difficulty, since he had reached retiring age in nineteen forty-eight. With the prospect of more years ahead of him than he had money enough comfortably to waste, he had turned to an old friend for aid; and Fabian Honeychurch, Professor of Child Health in the University of London and President of the Royal College of Paediatricians, had arranged for him to take charge of the College's small museum. Mr. Murivance had never taken an interest in children, parentally or professionally, but his gift for ferreting out details of provenance and identity fitted him sufficiently for his post.

"When I said she had been sent to the wrong address, I did not expect my meaning to be taken so literally. I feel her owner must have misunderstood our functions. She would do admirably for one of the other Royal Colleges."

"Admirably," Hilary agreed, and began to cast about for a way of escape. Mr. Murivance, once fairly started on a train of speculation, could waste an hour or two of his own and anyone else's time without a thought for the consequences. The consequences could not, of course, be very terrible; the College was a professional backwater, a period piece, a concession to academic indolence skilfully disguised as academic necessity. But Scott was young enough to prefer to think his work of some importance when he thought of it at all, and it was with real relief that he heard and recognised footsteps on the landing outside.

"There's my chief," he said briskly. "Good morning, Miles."

"Good morning, Hilary. Good morning, Mr. Murivance."

"Somebody has sent Mr. Murivance a skeleton."

Miles Latimer said, "I shouldn't like anyone to send me a skeleton. I should think of it as a memento mori."

"How Gothic of you, Miles! It wouldn't do for Mr. Murivance to look at things in that light. There are the evidences of mortality all around him."

Mr. Murivance glanced sideways at his familiar specimens as if seeing in them a new and more lurid significance. "There is a great deal of difference between a skeleton and a fragment in a glass pot," he said with a suggestion of disapproval. "Hamlet would hardly have lamented Yorick in the same terms if he had been handed one kidney or a section of liver."

"He couldn't have," Hilary said cheerfully, "not if you come to think of it. Now we had better leave you to your mystery, Mr. Murivance. We have a lot of work to get through this morning."

Outside the door of the room they shared on the third floor, Miles said, "What is Mr. Murivance's mystery, or is it too mysterious to be discussed?"

"He'll certainly discuss it," Hilary said with prophetic gloom. "We shall hear of nothing else for weeks. It seems he doesn't know who sent him the skeleton. I can't see that it matters much, personally. And we really have got a lot of work to do this morning, Miles, or I have, which is the same thing."

"I suppose I'd better take over some of it."

Latimer edited the *Journal of the Royal College of Paediatricians*. It was a quarterly publication, and each issue had to be submitted to a committee before it went to press. The clockwork regularity with which it received approval could never be taken wholly for granted, and anxiety about the fate of the latest edition marred Miles's days and added a certain excitement to Hilary's. Hilary's role of assistant was not as well defined as that of principal: He read articles, checked references, and turned the monumental ramblings of elderly contributors into an elegant, terse prose they generally accepted without surprise in proof.

On Hilary's desk were a pile of letters, a heap of proofs, a daily newspaper, a great many books on diseases of childhood. He picked up the newspaper and put it down again as he caught Miles's eye. "Prewitt's article?"

"Prewitt's article first. They've printed the chest X rays in the wrong order, and the fourth chart has a legend that has nothing to do with it."

"It doesn't belong to Prewitt at all. It comes from Savory Simpson's review of sepsis in day nurseries. I suppose the day nurseries have got Prewitt's leftovers. Yes, they have. I can't think how I came to mix them up. Day nurseries and branchial cysts have so little in common."

"So little that the printer's reader might have realised that the things didn't fit."

"It's kind of you to make excuses for me, Miles, because it looks so abject if I make them for myself. And I'm not nearly so ashamed as I should be, because my heart isn't in my work this morning. Now you must ask me why it isn't. If you don't, I shall tell you anyhow, and then I might feel I had made you the recipient of an unwanted confidence."

"Tell me anything you like," Miles said, but he was not listening.

Hilary took a deep breath. "I am going to be married. I am going to marry Kate Cardew. You shouldn't look surprised, Miles, even if you are. It is very rude to Kate and rather rude to me, and this is a difficult time for both of us."

"I didn't know I looked surprised," Miles said. This was disingenuous of him, for he had imagined himself to be Kate's future husband. He knew himself innocent of intentional rudeness, as he thought Hilary more eligible than himself and Kate too good for any man, himself included. He said, with an effort that fortunately went unperceived, "I hope you will be very happy, Hilary," and addressed himself immediately to the morning's work.

Fabian Honeychurch occupied a room on the fourth floor. He had chosen the room for himself with some misgivings. The president of the College, said his conscience, should occupy a large, imposing suite near the main entrance. Especially since there is no lift either for yourself or your distinguished visitors, added a more hedonistic inner voice. Exercise, something else prompted, might be a good thing for all of you. And this has always been the nicest room in the house, his memory said; and conscience had to retire before the force of this argument. For Honeychurch was the founder of the College as well as its first president, and the Queen Anne house in Caroline Square had been his own home. He had inherited it from a nonagenarian father at a time when only a very large income could have met its demands, and his income fell short of what was desired by several thousands. Sell the house he would not; so he made instead a philanthropic gesture of the first magnitude and was rewarded, as he couldn't have helped but hope, with the chance to spend a few of his working hours in what had once been a playroom for himself and his brothers. The round window in the circular room looked down on the square; standing by it, he could see all too clearly the determined raids of commerce on domesticity as year by year the frilled curtains retreated from the houses opposite, the brass plates advanced. But if he stayed, as he preferred to do, at his desk, only the highest branches of the planes and sycamores in the gardens were visible; hardly to be discerned when bare of leaf but suggesting in the spring a nonexistent panorama of woods surrounding the house; reminiscent always to one of his generation of hoops and nursemaids and white gloves. At ten in the morning on as cold a day as this he could hear voices of infant Honeychurches crossing the years on a rising wail of protest as mufflers were tied round necks, stout shoes were substituted for pumps, and the last sorrowful toddler was torn away from the inviting fireside. Nobody, he thought complacently, looking across his desk at the comfortable blaze in his grate, could tear him away now; but his secretary's gentle knock on the door a moment later broke upon his reverie as disturbingly as Nurse's summons to a walk. He was always pleased to see Miss Cardew: she charmingly followed her knock, her head a little bent with a diffidence far removed from her ordinary ease. She had come in on impulse with her scrap of personal news, and already felt more than half a fool for bothering him with it. The girl had an ironic style of beauty, very much her own, and hoped that this would be some com-

pensation for the break in the day's routine. By the time
Honeychurch had risen, correctly judging that this visit
was in some way out of the usual run, selected a chair for
her, poked the fire until it became imperative to open the
window to its fullest extent, she had begun to doubt
whether impulse had not led her unbecomingly astray. At
last she said, rather stiffly, sitting on the edge of her chair
as if she weren't twenty-four years old and always perfectly
controlled, "I'm engaged to be married, Professor Honeychurch. I am going to marry Hilary Scott at last, at long
last."

"It must seem long to Dr. Scott, I suppose," he said in
some astonishment. "It seems very sudden to me! I wish I
could think of the right thing to say, Miss Cardew. I hope
you will be very happy. Are you sure Hilary is the man you
want to marry?"

"That is not the right thing to say; almost anything else
would have been better! I suppose I'm sure," she said, and
felt suddenly that it had been quite sensible after all to
come and tell Honeychurch, for he had a perfect right to
know when his private secretary altered all her plans for a
strictly professional future. "Hilary isn't like anyone else,"
she said warmly, as if someone had been attacking him.
"He comes out well in most comparisons. He is only mod-
erately good-looking, and he isn't a man's man. But I'm
not a man myself, so that doesn't matter. And he is intelligent and kind and has a little money of his own, and he
appreciates Miles Latimer, which suggests that he is better
than I deserve."

"Why do you say that, Miss Cardew?"

"Because I'm rather ashamed of not appreciating Miles
myself. It shows a lack of real sensibility on my part."

"There was a rumour a few weeks ago," Honeychurch

said apologetically, for he was not as used to receiving female confidences as she had thought he might be, "that is to say, I imagined at one time that you might marry Dr. Latimer."

"Yes, and so did I. He never asked me."

"Would you have accepted him if he had?"

She considered for just long enough before replying to convince Honeychurch that the question was not so much of an impertinence as he had feared.

"No. I believe I have been in love with Hilary in a hopeless way for years."

"But you haven't known him for years," he reminded her.

"Nor I have. I wish I could get out of the habit of exaggeration."

She bit her lip, looking less sure of herself than ever. She was not, in fact, quite sure of either herself or Hilary; and when she left Honeychurch's room a few minutes later, she was no longer sure that she had been sensible in allowing the secret of her engagement to remain a secret for so short a time.

Miles Latimer was a man who passed unnoticed in large gatherings and hardly made his mark in small ones. He was thirty-eight and looked older; above the usual height, grey-haired, with uncertain features and an expression that could not be defined but suggested both kindness and reserve. His friends assumed that the reserve was due to a bitter experience of marriage, but they were wrong; it was in part the cause of his divorce and therefore could not be its result. The same quality might have lost him Kate, if there had ever been a chance of his gaining her, but he decided now that the chance had only existed in his own mind. His plans had to be changed, and he chose a course of action that demanded the use of powers more certainly his than the power of attracting women. He had thought for some time of beginning independent research, and now it seemed imperative to alter his daily life, to leave the College if possible and at least to escape the spectacle of Hilary's happiness. Some weeks before, he had laid a plan of investigation into the causes of congenital abnormalities of the lung before Professor Honeychurch, and at noon he went along to the president's room with an indefinite idea of pushing the matter to an issue.

"Sit down, Miles."

Honeychurch, a large man as old as Mr. Murivance, stood between his desk and the window and shadowed the room with his bulk. Miles could not see his face against the light, but the big head with the shiny brow, the spectacles, the remaining tufts of white hair above the ears were so familiar that he thought he did see them, and was surprised when the voice held a note of anxiety he had had no chance to detect in the unseen features.

"Is it about your project, Miles? I have put it before the Medical Research Council, as I said I would, and I am afraid they will not give you a grant. It was no use my telling them that you deserve their assistance more than the average young fool who likes to lay out money in expensive equipment simply to produce some piffling little thesis for average old fools like myself to yawn over. I tried to explain it to them, but they were indifferent and polite. The politeness showed me I was wasting my time."

"Is it because I have never done any research before?"

"Yes. They say you have had no training in modern laboratory methods. Of course they are rather specially careful about making grants just now. Public money is so much in the public eye."

Miles was silent.

"There are some other possible sources. Some of the big industrial firms have endowed studentships recently. But I believe they also prefer younger people."

"I can see why," Miles said thoughtfully. "They want to see a return for their money, and I can't promise that I shall ever be able to show them any."

Honeychurch sat down, and Miles added, "I mustn't take up any more of your time."

"Nor I of yours. Will the proofs be ready for the editorial board tomorrow? I know they will, I cannot think why I should have asked such a stupid question. If you do leave us, Miles, we shall miss you greatly. Much as Dr. Scott amuses me, I cannot think the *Journal* would be the same in his hands."

"Well, perhaps not quite the same. He writes far better than I do."

"But with no knowledge of his subject; together you constitute a remarkable team. Scott won't like working for Pounceforth."

"Pounceforth would take my place?" Miles said with a frown.

"I know he would like to. He has often told me so, and he is the darling of the appointments committee. Of course I have a casting vote, but I would not be given the chance of using it if he applied for the post."

"I wish it would be anyone else."

"Those are strong words, Miles, coming from you. You must comfort yourself with the knowledge that your departure is a necessary preliminary to his appointment: you will not have to share a room with him, as Scott will."

"Pounceforth is a man of wide interests," Miles said unwillingly. "He is even an antiquarian in a small way. He digs up Roman villas and carries coins about in his pockets to jingle at people."

"I can see why you dislike him. Honeychurch said. "It must be because he carries coins around. We had better get you some of your own to jingle. I will speak to Roberts and see if the College can do anything."

"I thought the College was practically penniless?"

"Certainly our revenues hardly compare with those of the older Colleges, but we have a little, if it isn't all tied up in various ways. We will do our best."

Dr. Pounceforth and Professor Honeychurch sat at luncheon in the small refectory, on the ground floor. Two-dimensional female angels hovered upon the ceiling; a solid male attendant brought the soup and hovered over their heads at a more mundane level. Mr. Roberts, the College's financial secretary, joined them with a conspiratorial air and his usual good appetite.

"So Miles Latimer is leaving us." This was how he had interpreted Honeychurch's enquiries about a possible loan to support original research.

"Surely not?" Pounceforth said coolly."Can he bear to tear himself away from young Scott?"

"Dr. Scott is getting married," Honeychurch remarked. "He is marrying Miss Cardew. She told me this morning." He did not add that he was at once touched and perplexed at having been told, and suspected that the girl would have chosen an elderly male relative to talk to if she had had such a person near at hand. This habit of underestimating his own importance curiously contributed to Honeychurch's popularity; the same habit in Miles led simply to his being underestimated.

"That explains the other," Pounceforth said with a nod. "Latimer could never bear to watch Scott in the throes of love for a mere woman."

"I have never seen any evidence of an unusual degree of attachment between Scott and Latimer," Honeychurch said placidly.

"I was speaking not of degree but kind."

"Then, you would do better not to speak at all."

Victor Pounceforth returned to his half-eaten sole. He was librarian to the College; a man of over forty, but younger in appearance, with a thatch of straight brown hair and smooth, babyish cheeks held in shape by a bland, rosy skin. His face gave no hint of the acerbity of his nature, but those who knew him best were quick to read the evidence of his more spiteful thoughts in a slightly heightened flush. He disliked Miles for no good reason, and Hilary Scott as a matter of principle, because he was young, had money, and was now a successful lover into the bargain. He allowed a moment for the chill produced by Honeychurch's rebuke to lapse and said, "Now, Roberts, can we hear the details? Why is Latimer leaving? Where is he going? Who will take his place?"

"He is leaving because he wants to investigate lung abnormalities; it will require all his time for the next three years, so he will have to resign from the *Journal*. And he cannot afford to be entirely without salary or prospects, so he will have to return to clinical practice and take his chances on getting the facilities he needs at some hospital or other."

"It won't be easy for a man of his age," Honeychurch said slowly, more to himself than to the others.

"A man of whose age?"

"Sit down, Murivance," Roberts said, indicating an empty chair. "Have the sole, not the mutton. We are talking about Latimer and his future. At thirty-eight it is really very enterprising of him to have a future at all, at any rate one different from his past."

Mr. Murivance sat down and ordered fish. The refectory was very full. He looked about him. "Latimer is not lunching with us today."

"He probably isn't hungry," Pounceforth said. "What with his age and the uncertainty about his future and Miss Cardew's engagement to Dr. Scott it would be surprising if he had an appetite. But why is he going?" he asked, suddenly reverting to an earlier question. "Couldn't he work here? There is plenty of room on the third floor, and surely he could get a grant for his equipment?"

"That is just what he cannot do," Roberts said. "Between us, it is lack of money that will hold him back. Honeychurch has approached the Medical Research Council on his behalf and they are not interested."

"There is nobody whose powers I respect more highly than Latimer's," said Pounceforth in a tone which cast some doubt upon the truth of this statement, "but I don't see him impressing a committee with the force of his personality. I speak as one with considerable experience of committees from both sides of the table." He succeeded in conveying that he had been equally impressive upon either side.

"So Latimer is short of money? Oh, dear," said Mr. Murivance, "if you could pass the sauce, Honeychurch, thank you so much. Now, that is not a thing I would have guessed."

"You might have," Honeychurch said heavily. "Nearly everyone else has guessed it, knowing his salary."

"The College cannot afford high rates of remuneration," Roberts said. "And his is the sort of post that would have been honorary a generation or two back."

"It might as well be honorary now, for all the good Latimer gets out of it."

"The College can hardly be expected to support Latimer's ex-wives," Pounceforth said, "and a high proportion of his salary is diverted to that end."

There was silence; Mr. Murivance was unable to restrain himself for more than a few moments. "I thought he had only been married once?"

"Once or twice, I hardly know which. His affairs are of no particular interest to me."

Honeychurch put in: "They should not be, but they clearly are. If you wish to spread gossip, Pounceforth, you cannot permit yourself to be disinterested, let alone accurate. William, I am going to the smoking room to drink my coffee."

Roberts followed Honeychurch out, but not willingly.

"Latimer's wife divorced him; there was collusion; she was undoubtedly the guilty party," Pounceforth said in a hurried, penetrating voice. "He was fool enough to take the blame and pay her alimony."

"He behaved like a gentleman," said Mr. Murivance sufficiently. "I am sorry to hear that he is poor. Would you recommended the flan, Pounceforth, or shall I merely ask for cheese?"

"Have both; I did."

At the foot of the stairs, Kate Cardew stopped for a moment to look in her handbag. Pounceforth came up to her.

"I hear you are to be married, Miss Cardew. Dr. Latimer is a very fortunate man."

She showed her surprise and immediately wished she had hidden it. "He may be, Dr. Pounceforth, I cannot tell. I am engaged to Hilary Scott."

Pounceforth stood quite still on the step above her; this gave him an advantage he did not ordinarily have, as she was a tall girl. "But, Miss Cardew—Kate, if I may—surely I haven't been mistaken? It seemed to me that you had a decided preference for Dr. Latimer. Was I wrong?"

"You must see you were. I don't know what could have given you such an idea. I hope nobody else has been so wide of the mark."

"I hope Latimer himself has not."

"I suppose," she said, thinking hard, "it is because you've noticed us together sometimes. Of course it is noticeable when Miles is seen with a woman, because it happens so rarely. If anyone else has made the same mistake, perhaps you will set them right."

"I shall be very sorry to have to do so. I had hoped—but of course Latimer isn't a free man, not in the full sense of the word. He could hardly have expected you to share his reduced circumstances. I hope nobody has been foolish enough or unkind enough to offer him congratulations."

"If you haven't been unkind enough, Dr. Pounceforth, I cannot believe anyone else would be."

She looked splendid in a rage; Miles saw her from the landing above and caught his breath, not knowing why she was angry. Indeed she did not quite know herself; possibly Pounceforth knew.

II

"So you are really going, Latimer?" Roberts said some days later.

"Going? Going where? I am not going anywhere that I know of."

"Honeychurch seemed to think you would be leaving to do your research."

"He was kinder to me than I deserve," Miles said slowly. "I did have some idea of that sort, but things have turned out differently. It looks as if I shall stay here for the rest of my days correcting Savory Simpson's redundancies of style and subject. How inglorious I make it sound!"

"It is rather inglorious. But nobody else would do it as well as you do."

"That's what Honeychurch said. I must say it's nice to hear it again, and from an independent source. Sit down, Roberts; Hilary won't be wanting his desk again this afternoon, and I have reached a point at which I might even throw myself out of the window if there were nobody here to stop me."

Roberts glanced at the window with a look of rapid calculation. He was a cautious man and one accustomed to weighing all statements made to him with great care. Seeing that Miles was not even smiling, that what he had just said was in fact no joke and perhaps not even an exaggeration, he became ill at ease and tried to cover his feeling with brusqueness.

"I never heard you talk like that before, Latimer. You do not usually dramatise yourself."

"From now on I intend to. I have lost one wife and failed to gain another, and I am a disappointed aspirant to scientific glory. There is material for drama in all that."

"There is material for a breakdown certainly," Roberts said. "You had better have one and be done with it: you are not much use to anyone in that state."

"Roberts, don't you know how untrue it is that you have to be cruel to be kind? It is almost a worse lie than the one about the darkest hour being just before the dawn."

"One can hardly be sure of that until the dawn comes," Roberts said, adding, he feared, sententiousness to lack of sympathy.

"I can," Miles said resignedly. "I have seen a good many dawns lately."

"So that's what is wrong. I thought it might be. Why don't you take a sedative? What nonsense I talk! Sedatives are not at all what you need. Violent activity would be more to the point."

"I have done my best to be violently active. In the last few days I have written to everyone I can think of to ask for money or advice or both. There has been some advice, not worth taking. Of course any money would have been worth taking but nobody has offered it. There is no post for me at any of the teaching hospitals. I have had to withdraw my resignation. Did you know that I had resigned?"

"Pounceforth told me."

"Yes, he would have done. I think he was hoping to take my place, and now he must be disappointed. I wish I could feel sorry about it for his sake, but I only feel it for my own."

"Couldn't you ask Prentice to help you? He is interested in the subject himself. You could work in the museum gallery. You would probably only get a little way without equipment, but it would be something."

"No, I have thought of that; but working in the museum means Mr. Murivance and his skeleton peering over one's shoulder all the time, and I don't think much good would come of it. No, Roberts, I can't possibly do anything worthwhile here unless somebody leaves me a little fortune. And I don't see any likelihood of that."

"You shouldn't do it, Mr. Murivance, indeed you shouldn't. There is not the slightest need. Matheson is always here if I am not. I don't like to say it, but you are too advanced in years to climb upon stepladders and lift down these heavy specimen jars. I can see that you are a good deal shaken, and no wonder! Come and sit down for a few minutes and I will send Matheson for some tea."

Prentice, a young man prematurely bald and wise, led Mr. Murivance across the museum into their small office, stooped to light the gas fire, and sent the museum attendant to the dining room for a tray.

"I believe you have twisted your bad shoulder again! I cannot turn my back for a moment but you insist on leaping from shelf to shelf as if you were a mere lad. Let this be a lesson to you!"

"You are making it one," Mr. Murivance said, but his shoulder was very painful and he was inclined to agree with his assistant's strictures, though he resented them. The tea tray appeared, followed by Professor Honeychurch and Hilary Scott.

"Theodore, Matheson tells me that you have had a fall; it is too bad of you to make a disturbance down here; you know my room is directly overhead. Promise you will do no more of this undignified clambering. Dr. Prentice, see to it that he does not."

"I have been saying just the same thing, Professor Honeychurch, only without quite your rallying note. What should we do without Mr. Murivance?"

"What indeed? I see Matheson has brought up some muffins. Do you think there are enough for all of us?"

"I will get some more," Matheson said in simple resignation.

"Hadn't we better arrange to have that shoulder X-rayed?" Prentice whispered to Mr. Murivance with the intention of arousing further solicitude in others as well as displaying it himself.

"There is not the slightest need to fuss about my shoulder."

"Did you fall upon it?"

"Yes, Honeychurch, I did, upon the point, and the point is—oh, I have made a pun! I can see Dr. Scott, pretending to writhe in agony, but he must sometimes have made puns himself—yes. The point is that this shoulder has troubled me before today. I have a mild degree of fibrositis in the muscles around the joint."

Honeychurch expressed himself sorry to hear this.

"Mr. Murivance diminishes its importance," Prentice said, this being the reverse of his own intention. "I know it has inconvenienced him a great deal of late."

"It has been wet, very wet. The weather, I mean," Mr. Murivance mildly complained.

"He has had to have treatment for it."

"These muffins are splendid," Honeychurch said. "What sort of treatment?"

"He goes to Sidney Berringer," Prentice said on a note of dubiety.

Hilary and Honeychurch exchanged glances.

"Isn't he a quack?" Hilary said.

"He is medically qualified. He has beds at St. Jude's. He is a leading orthopaedic surgeon. Nobody could be less of a quack."

"Yes, but doesn't he have extraordinary fads about treatment and do all sorts of unorthodox things?"

"That is how medicine advances," Prentice said primly.

"Yes, that is one of the ways, but not the best, do you think? What does he do to your shoulder, Mr. Murivance?"

"Well, Scott, he usually injects a little local anaesthetic around the joint and then puts it through a full range of movement. Afterwards I am hardly aware that I have suffered at all."

"There is nothing unusual about that treatment," Hilary said, as if in disappointment.

"What is chiefly unusual about Mr. Berringer is his manner," Prentice explained.

"Have you, too, had the benefit of his manipulations?"

"No, only of his manner, and that only in public meetings and at professional dinners. He has great charm and a remarkable presence. His methods perhaps admit of some criticism, but his personality must have a healing effect on all who come into contact with him."

"It is for his methods and not his personality that I go to him," Mr. Murivance said. "He has helped me a great deal. It would be ungrateful in me to deny it. Perhaps,

Prentice, you would be kind enough to telephone him for me and make an appointment for six o'clock this evening."

While Prentice went to the telephone, Honeychurch rose and stood by the skeleton. "You still have no idea where she comes from, Theodore?"

"I have made some enquiries," Mr. Murivance said. "I have mentioned her to one or two people and received no information that I could rely on. Our colleagues in Lincoln's Inn Fields were not expecting her. I have spoken to my counterpart at the Royal College of Physicians and he assures me that they are as unused to getting anonymous donations as I am."

"If you have no news for us by the end of the week, I think it might be as well to insert a paragraph in the *Lancet* and perhaps in one of the national newspapers. 'Sincere gratitude to an unknown benefactor' or something of that sort."

Hilary said, "I don't see how we can say we are sincerely grateful when we partly wish to trace the giver in order to return his gift."

"I'm sure Dr. Scott will write us something with the correct note of wistful regret," Prentice said handsomely.

"What are we going to do with her if she is never claimed?" Hilary asked. "Would your friends in Lincoln's Inn Fields find her acceptable? Did they sound envious of our good fortune?"

"Far from it," Mr. Murivance said with a decisive shake of his head. "Newcastle is not likely to be grateful when people carry coals to it."

"The Anatomy Department at University College might like an extra skeleton," Honeychurch suggested. "Some of the students could come and fetch her. They seem to enjoy carrying unsuitable objects through the streets in broad daylight."

"Let us all think of someone we really hate," Hilary said, "and send her to him with a label saying not to be opened until Christmas." He added regretfully, after a moment's pregnant silence, "But Pounceforth wouldn't really be shocked by a skeleton."

Mr. Murivance left the building at half past four. He walked northwards up Southampton Row and found a taxicab in Woburn Place. He was driven at no great speed down the Euston Road and into the drab network of turnings between Fitzroy Square and Great Portland Street. Stopping his driver outside a small house—one of a well-preserved terrace now mostly converted into offices—Mr. Murivance paid his fare and added a tip which he but not the driver considered munificent, and opened the front door while his forefinger was still pressing a bell marked EUSTACE TRIMBLE: ANATOMICAL SUPPLIES. He was met in the cold, dark passage by a man about his own age, short and plethoric, very bald, and too obese to manage the single flight of stairs before them without a little breathlessness. In a room on the first floor they sat down; Mr. Murivance explained his mission and asked his question.

"These days there is very little demand for whole skeletons. Students cannot afford them and of course they are not necessary," Mr. Trimble said, modestly condoling with students. "An arm, a leg, a skull, perhaps a vertebral column and a pelvis—but a whole articulated skeleton would be a luxury."

"So it is quite possible you would remember if you had supplied one, a young female one, to some client or other during recent months?"

"Oh, it is more than possible, it is quite certain! I have an order book here."

"Would it be a breach of professional secrecy if I were to ask you to look out the name for me?"

"I don't see why it should be. The element of mystery about the whole thing suggests to me that it may be a hoax, and if so it is a very expensive one and the joker may not be at all sorry to have his property returned. I will give you the order book, Mr. Murivance, and you can look at it yourself. There might be a name there that means something to you. I have a little work to do in the next room."

Mr. Murivance turned over the pages of the order book; when the other returned, he was still sitting with the book open on his lap, but there was a change in his expression that Mr. Trimble could not define.

"I have found a name that means something to me, to borrow your phrase."

"Then, your time hasn't been wasted in coming here. I am so glad!"

"And I hardly feel as glad as I should be, but I suppose it is better to have no mysteries. Please tell me one thing more, Trimble. Would you be likely to send a skeleton to its purchaser in a cabin trunk?"

"No, we certainly would not. We have carefully constructed wooden crates with the name of the firm stamped on them."

"Yes, that is what I thought. So there is still something to be explained. I see I was too easily satisfied."

But when Mr. Trimble recalled this brief conversation later, he did not believe that the change on his friend's face had been one of simple satisfaction.

"Come along in, Mr. Murivance! Come along in and make yourself thoroughly at home! My receptionist has gone, she is always in a hurry to get away, as if this wasn't the driest and the warmest and the pleasantest place on a November night!"

Sidney Berringer appeared to make large claims for his consulting rooms, but the rooms themselves were large and the claims seemed justified to Mr. Murivance, who had walked nearly the length of Great Portland Street and much of Wigmore Street, rather than take two taxis in a single evening. The inner room was very high, well carpeted, well lit, and a coal fire burned brightly in the grate. Sidney Berringer put more coal upon it while he was speaking, and his beautiful fat white hands upon the tongs seemed to Mr. Murivance the symbol of a Promethean power for bringing comfort into the lives of men. Berringer did not display the tools of his trade, as a more vulgar practitioner might; his examination couch was covered in striped satin, his hand basin was hidden behind a screen, he wrote sitting at a lady's bureau using a quill on paper like that of which banknotes are made. He was not personally prepossessing, as he had not the warm red colour that generally goes with plump middle age; indeed he accentuated his pallor with a dusting of powder, just as he enhanced his splendid clothes with a sparing use of the perfume bottle. In his presence, Mr. Murivance seemed thinner and older and more shabby than ever: it may have been a tribute to the goodness of Berringer's heart that he welcomed this elderly waif as if he were a favourite wealthy patient with a rare and fascinating disease.

"It is your shoulder again. You see there is no need to tell me, I saw it all in your face as you came in, looking so tired and cold! Now sit down by the fire, and when you feel warm enough just slip off your coat and we will see what can be done."

"I fell upon it today," Mr. Murivance said, taking off his coat as he spoke.

"Fell upon it, what's that! You dared to fall upon that shoulder, when I must have told you a thousand times to take care of it! What disobedience, what carelessness! What are we to do with you? I really think I shall have to punish you a little bit just to remind you that my advice is to be taken."

Mr. Murivance laughed, but not with real mirth, because Berringer's fingers exploring the tender spots in his muscles seemed less gentle than usual.

"Now, where does it hurt, exactly? There, I see, and there, and a little bit here, too, but not so much. Pull your chair up close to the fire while I fetch my syringe and the procaine solution and then we shall have you right in a jiffy."

He brought the syringe and some needles and an enamel dish together with a small rubber-capped bottle and some swabs soaked in spirit. Then he went behind the screen and washed his hands. Mr. Murivance did not distinctly hear his first words on returning and excused himself for his lack of attention.

"It was nothing. I asked you a question but you didn't hear it, and it was not of any account."

Mr. Murivance asked for the question to be repeated, as he was clearly expected to do.

"I merely asked if you had looked any further into the provenance of your skeleton."

"Did I bore even you with that story? Yes, I know who it came from, or at least I have good reason to think I do."

"And who was it?"

"Well, it doesn't turn out to be anyone very interesting. It was a colleague of mine."

"A colleague of yours, really! Just pull your vest away from your shoulder, Mr. Murivance, and I will make the first injection."

Mr. Murivance complied. There was a cold, soothing sensation as Berringer dabbed the skin with spirit, then the prick of the needle and a more prolonged discomfort that ended with a dragging feeling as the needle came out.

"And who is this generous colleague, Mr. Murivance? Have you thanked him yet? Was he put out by your brilliant sleuthing?"

Mr. Murivance said, with a small gasp for the second and third injections, "I only made the discovery on my way here. I shall tax him with it tomorrow. It was Pounceforth, our librarian." The fourth injection went a little deeper, he thought. "And now I come to think of it, you have a right to be interested. I forgot that you know Victor Pounceforth."

"Oh, I think you are mistaken, Mr. Murivance! I have heard you mention him, I daresay I have seen his name in the journals, but I have never met Pounceforth in my life."

"That was not one of the tender places," Mr. Murivance said peevishly after the fifth injection, "but it is now. I cannot understand why you deny knowing Pounceforth. It was he who sent me to you. It is very unbecoming in you to forget someone who does you a good office, even if the good office does turn out to be a mixed blessing."

"You mustn't describe yourself as a mixed blessing," Berringer said in an absent tone. He stood a little way off looking thoughtfully at the five minute spots of blood on Mr. Murivance's shoulder.

"And Pounceforth told me," Mr. Murivance said, aware that this encounter with Berringer was not going as smoothly as others of the same kind, "that he had seen you at Throckleford while he was mapping out the site of the villa. He gave me the impression that you, too, were interested in Roman remains. But of course you must be! The last time I was here I remember I borrowed——"

But it was obvious that Berringer was not listening. "And Pounceforth sent you the skeleton?" he said abruptly.

"It is not as simple as that. He bought the skeleton, but I don't know that he sent it to me. It came differently packed from the way it was delivered to him."

"He might have changed it."

"Yes, he might have," Mr. Murivance admitted. "I am making a mystery where there is none, I daresay. I expect you remember him now."

"I believe I do. I see there is no more procaine in this bottle. I shall get some from the other room. Stay as you are, Mr. Murivance, I will be back in a moment."

He took his empty syringe with him, and when he came back it was already filled.

"Another half-empty bottle. So I filled my syringe outside and threw both away together. And now, where is that other bad place?"

His fingers probed with discreet hostility until he found the right spot, and then he made the last injection.

"Just go and lie down upon the couch for a minute, Mr. Murivance, and that will give the procaine time to work before I do the manipulation."

"Your attentions are a great comfort to me," Mr. Murivance said, but was not entirely comfortable all the same.

III

Four days later, Hilary Scott came into the museum to find Prentice and Roberts deep in discussion while Pounceforth examined some specimens absorbedly in the background.

"Are you talking about Miles's bequest? I am so glad, because that's what I want to talk about. It is the best news I have heard since my engagement."

"It is not perhaps quite so satisfactory a thing in some ways," Prentice said, his voice, rather than his words, conveying a mild reproach. "We have lost a much-valued colleague, and that must give our rejoicing a little undercurrent of sadness."

"Of course it is sad, but not as sad as all that. Mr. Murivance had no relatives or friends; otherwise there would have been nothing for Miles. And he could not have hoped to live much longer in the course of things."

"Scott, you forget that one of your audience is over fifty. You cannot expect everyone to be so unconcerned at the course of things as you are."

"I am not fifty yet, but I must associate myself with Roberts on that point," Pounceforth remarked.

His words had their not infrequent effect of putting an end to the conversation for a moment; but Prentice wanted information and was determined to get it. He turned pointedly to Hilary.

"Did Mr. Murivance never give Latimer a hint of it?"

"No, Miles was as surprised as we are. He is still more surprised than glad. Perhaps being glad will come later."

"There is nobody," Prentice said warmly, "who would make better use of the money. I don't suppose there is a great deal?"

"Since he didn't know there was to be any, it would be more than enough."

But Prentice was nothing if not persistent. "I have heard it put variously at six hundred and six thousand pounds. I expect it is nearer the first?"

"It is, but only a little nearer," Roberts said. He hated to be ignorant about other people's money and would not pretend to be so merely in order to appear less worldly than Prentice. "It is about two thousand eight hundred pounds, and there are some personal belongings as well. It would be silly to think of Latimer as a wealthy man, but this will certainly make a difference."

"Is there anyone here to whom it would *not* make a difference?" Pounceforth asked, neatly killing the conversation for a second time.

A faint but heartening sunlight illuminated their faces the next moment and was reflected off many glass surfaces. Matheson was dusting pots on the top shelf.

"What is to be done with the skeleton?" Roberts said, watching a downward flick of the duster.

"She is to stay here," Prentice told him. "I have spoken to Professor Honeychurch and he thinks it best to let the matter rest. If people will be careless with their property, it is not for other people to try to remedy the fault beyond a certain point."

"The certain point being in this case Murivance's death. Well, the skeleton can hardly expect to occupy everyone's attention as completely as she did his. We were all of us sick and tired of her long ago."

"Roberts, I suspect you of being callous towards the departed, and you haven't my excuse of being callow as well."

"Do you think your excuse is a matter for pride, Scott? Is this a time to be cheaply witty?"

"I don't know that it is, Pounceforth, but then, I don't know that that was what I was being."

"We cannot very long maintain an attitude of reverence towards Mr. Murivance's memory," Prentice said simply.

"No, we cannot," Pounceforth agreed with some severity. "It is less than a week since he died and the attitude has not survived him by that long."

"He was an able, kindly man, and in some ways he will be missed. I don't see that we have to make more of it than that."

"We can always rely on you, Roberts," Pounceforth said, "to restrain us from an unworthy indulgence in feelings. You show us how much better it is to speak truthfully, even if the truth is not altogether to our credit. I own that I myself was more affected than I would have believed possible. I went to the funeral this morning; Latimer was there and Honeychurch. It was moving, as grander ceremonies are not. Latimer and Honeychurch had lunch together and I stopped for a while at the graveside."

"That was a beautiful gesture," Prentice said.

"Yes, that is what it was. It served no purpose save to allow you to make Miles and Honeychurch look heartless. You have already made Roberts and myself sound so, and if you will only set to work at once upon Prentice you will soon be isolated in your grief, which is what you seem to want."

"Of course you are not entirely heartless," Pounceforth said, in a tone of frank consideration. "It is natural for you to feel more elated over your friend's good fortune, Scott, than distressed over what has brought it about. And that must be true of Latimer as well."

"Yes, it must be," Roberts said. "Neither Scott nor Latimer is a hypocrite."

Pounceforth stood up and took the hand of the skeleton with a gesture of purest familiarity. "It is a strange thing," he said easily, allowing the fleshless fingers to lie upon his own, "that Latimer should have told Mr. Murivance that this skeleton was a memento mori."

"Did he tell him that? Did Murivance tell you so?"

"No, Roberts, I forget who told me. It was the sort of carelessly unkind remark a younger man might make to an older one. Of course Latimer did not know that Murivance had remembered him in his will, did he? If he had known, one would not dismiss the remark as careless."

"It was not careless, nor was it unkind," Hilary said swiftly. "Miles would say what he did because he is a man who cares for the implications of things."

"He has not a monopoly in implications," Pounceforth said, achieving a higher note. "I care for them too, as you can see. I would have said that that remark implied a certain determination that the hearer should be reminded of death. But perhaps I read it wrongly. And I remember now that it was you who told me, Scott. Prentice was present and Matheson. I could not have asked for more impartial witnesses or a more disinterested informant."

"I don't think the information is important enough to require witnesses."

"But I think you do, Scott. It seems to me that you are unnecessarily impressed by it. I didn't mean to upset you so much when I passed on our little scrap of knowledge. I would not have passed it on at all if I had guessed how much you had already read into it. I only said that Latimer's remark was careless, but you almost seem to suggest that there was deliberate malice in it."

Hilary went up to Honeychurch shaking with rage, an emotion he had scarcely felt before and found not so exhilarating as it is generally thought to be. Honeychurch was not altogether surprised at the visit, as he believed in maintaining an atmosphere of informality within the College, but he was more than surprised when he learned the reason for it.

"Professor Honeychurch, I suppose you cannot get rid of Pounceforth?"

"What an extraordinary request! I beg you to think what you are saying, Dr. Scott. Or think what you are asking me to say, which is more to the point. I can hardly discuss one of your senior colleagues with you."

Hilary stood up, having only just sat down, and Honeychurch perceived the rage and inexcusably succumbed to his temptation to share it.

"Pounceforth is a man who knows how to make himself appear invaluable to committees, and I am answerable to several committees for my changes in staff. I have had the very devil of a job to persuade them to let Dr. Latimer retain his post as editor while he gets on with his research, and I was only able to do it, I will tell you quite frankly, Dr. Scott, by assuring them that Pounceforth would deputise for him for the next three years."

"But he has been putting out revolting rumours about Miles and Mr. Murivance," Hilary burst out; "he says that Miles knew he was to be left some money."

"I suppose he may have known," Honeychurch said guardedly.

"Miles says he did not and I believe him. And Pounceforth goes further: he practically accused Miles of hastening Mr. Murivance's end."

Honeychurch emerged from behind the wing of his armchair. "Is this true? Has Pounceforth dared to suggest that murder has been committed?"

"It would not be murder in any ordinary sense of the word; but he is telling everybody that Miles told the old gentleman to think of that skeleton as a memento mori, and he has even gone so far as to hint that Miles himself might have sent it."

"What does Pounceforth think Mr. Murivance died of? A broken heart?"

"I haven't asked him. It cannot have been any of the common conditions, because the postmortem showed nothing out of the ordinary."

"How I hate this backbiting and slander!" Honeychurch said with unaccustomed vehemence. "Pounceforth has said nothing to Dr. Latimer directly, I take it?"

"He hardly needs to. It will come round to Miles in the end."

"I see we were too ready to accept the money as a godsend. There were conditions attached to it we did not anticipate."

"That must be true of anything unexpected. You still don't think you can get rid of Pounceforth?"

"It is out of the question," Honeychurch said regretfully. "He knows that I have confidence in Dr. Latimer and so do my various committees. It would only be putting another weapon into his hands if I showed myself willing to persecute him. But if I hear any more of this I shall see him and tell him what I think."

"I doubt if that would have much effect," Hilary said with a sense of anticlimax and futility.

"I am sure it will have none. But I cannot deny myself the satisfaction of being thoroughly savage to him. I wish Dr. Latimer were likely to be thoroughly savage on his own behalf. It would teach Pounceforth a much-needed lesson."

Hilary shook his head. "Miles will never defend himself; he is defective in every way. I cannot see why we are all so fond of him, unless it is because his imperfections show us how much better we are. And of course we are not really much better. We are only different, and Pounceforth is different again."

"Well, Scott, I hope we shall work well together and make a success of our partnership. I don't think you will find me a more difficult taskmaster than Latimer. In some ways I may be more exacting, but you will soon accustom yourself to my idiosyncrasies."

Pounceforth had some difficulty in making this speech; he found it impossible to achieve a note of spontaneity in good will, which came easily to him at other times. Hilary added something to the difficulty by continuing to sit at his desk while Pounceforth addressed him. He seemed not to see Pounceforth's outstretched hand, and it was soon withdrawn.

"I have proffered the olive branch and you have not accepted it. I will not have it said of me that I harbour grudges."

"Clearly it is a thing that I will have said of me quite soon now, as soon as you go to have your coffee."

"I do not intend to have any coffee this morning. I have to make myself thoroughly acquainted with the arrangements here."

"You won't mind if I go?"

"We will see about that when the time comes."

"It is half past ten now."

"We will see about coffee when the time comes."

Silence fell. Hilary tapped gently upon his desk with a forefinger. Pounceforth picked up various sheets of paper, read them, and laid them down.

"Here is an unsolicited article from a registrar in Sheffield. I see Latimer has marked it with a tick. What does that mean?"

"What you would think. The article is to go in the next issue."

"But it is about tuberculous meningitis. This quarter's *Journal* contained an article by Professor Walton on the same subject. I cannot think this redundancy is good for our circulation."

"Our circulation is stationary. The Members of the College receive copies free of charge. It isn't on sale to the general public."

"But we have readers, and they must not be bored."

"The article is original and unorthodox. Miles thought it would make a good contrast to Walton's."

"I do not think so much of it. And it seems to me almost insolent to set a young and inexperienced man's opinions up against those of an authority. We shall not publish work of this caliber in future."

"I see we shall not. It is a good thing that our circulation is no more likely to fall than to rise."

"Scott, in Latimer's day, what precisely did you do in this office?"

"I sat with my feet upon the desk whistling airs from the ballet. That is what you want me to say, and I will show you I am not behindhand in meeting your wishes."

"I imagine you performed some small, routine tasks to justify the salary you received?"

"They must have been very small indeed to justify my salary. Yes, Pounceforth, I did. I checked references. I read proofs. I was responsible for maintaining our good relations with the printers."

"I would not have thought it your métier. I would have hazarded a guess that something less pedestrian might have suited your talents better."

"No, you are confusing me with Latimer. It is he who has ideas above his station. I am quite happy to be a sort of superior office boy."

"Latimer shouldn't have allowed you to stay at that level. You must be encouraged to live up to your own highest standards."

"You do not understand me at all, Pounceforth. My standards are lower than you would believe possible."

"I see that Latimer's must have been very low indeed."

"It's high time we stopped talking about Miles."

"Yes, it is. I have had Latimer, Latimer, Latimer thrown at me ever since I entered this room. Of course I am well aware that I shall never be able to fill his place. I do not command the sort of veneration people hold him in."

"Do people hold Miles in veneration?" Hilary said in simple wonder. "I would not have thought that. I knew people liked him, but that sounds much more ordinary. It's queer that I speak of him in the past tense. I suppose it is because I shall never work for him again."

"He will take over from me three years from now."

"Well, yes, but I shall not be here. I doubt if our partnership will last as long as that, Pounceforth. And I am not sure that Miles will ever come back. If his work is successful, he will go on to something else. It is the first step into research that is so difficult."

"But Latimer is a very fortunate man. Nobody could have thought that Mr. Murivance would act upon so slight a hint."

Hilary got up so quickly that Pounceforth involuntarily recoiled. "I did not think I should be here in three years' time, and now I see I shall not last the three months until our next publication. It will be hard for you to manage with an assistant as inexperienced as yourself, but that is what you will have to do."

"Where are you going, Scott? It is hardly time for coffee yet!"

"You can be obtuse, Pounceforth, when it suits you. It is a pity that it does not suit you more often. I'm going to Honeychurch to hand in my resignation. I find I deserve to be accused of harbouring grudges. It is a thing I intend to do from this time forward."

"So that's why I'm going, Kate. I hope you understand it all."

"I can see why you cannot work with Pounceforth, though I believe I should have given it a longer trial. But women are generally known to be less sensitive than men."

"Do you think the worse of me?"

"I have not had time to think at all yet. What shall you do?"

"I mean to devote myself to the destruction of Pounceforth. I shall throw a bomb at him when the editorial board meets. I shall send him papers copied from other journals under the names of deceased physicians. I shall bribe the compositors to print obscene verses at the head of his leading articles. I shall retire into the country and breed pigs. You will love pigs, Kate."

"I am not sure that I shall. I am not sure that I will marry you if you have no fixed occupation."

"But how can there be a more fixed occupation than breeding pigs? It will make a man of me. Kate, you are joking."

"No, I am serious. I am very fond of you, Hilary, but that is partly because of your touch with the *Journal*."

"Even without the *Journal* you might find my touch pleasant."

"I don't want to live in the country. I don't want to spend my days among pigs and my evenings at the Women's Insitute."

"That is not where you would spend your evenings."

"Hilary, I think it is infantile and absurd of you to give up interesting work for a mere prejudice."

"My prejudice against Pounceforth is anything but mere. At the moment it is my ruling passion."

"That doesn't leave much room for me; it seems to leave room only for Miles. You are not at school any longer, Hilary! You do not have to fag for the older boys."

"That was a thing I successfully avoided at school. Kate, I believe you are jealous of Miles. It is unworthy of you."

"Unworthy, unworthy! I know it is unworthy! I know that I cannot understand your friendship, that I don't like you to lose your job because you cannot hold your tongue about another man's virtues. And I cannot understand the virtues, either. Miles has simply inherited some money; he needed it very badly; Mr. Murivance knew he needed it. It would not have been so remarkable if Mr. Murivance had died to help him."

"People cannot die just by wishing to, Kate."

"They can kill themselves."

"He didn't kill himself, you know he did not."

"He came back here the night after he fell down in the museum and they found him dead there in the morning. If he felt ill, he could have called for help. There was a telephone, there were other people in the building."

"He may have died suddenly. That's what the coroner said at the inquest."

"But there was no certain cause for sudden death; that's what the coroner said too. He was an old man, and he was alone in that place with all those things around him and the skeleton that Miles called a reminder of death, and he didn't call for help."

"You have been listening to Pounceforth," Hilary said, knowing himself beaten.

"Yes, I have."

"You cannot listen to me as well." Later he said, "This is not the sort of thing lovers usually quarrel about."

"It is almost as if we are not lovers."

"Then, perhaps we are not lovers anymore."

IV

"Latimer, I wonder if you would do me a favour."

"If it is in my power, Pounceforth."

"You will be working in the museum gallery this afternoon?"

"For an hour or two at least," Miles told him.

"It is just this: I have mislaid some notes, just odd jottings on a small pad of pink paper. I rather think I last had them when I was talking to Prentice the day before yesterday. I am so busy at the moment, if you or Matheson or Prentice himself would just glance around the place for me, it would be doing me a kindness."

"A very little kindness. I will see what I can do."

Miles left the small refectory, crossed the hall with a more buoyant step than he had formerly used, and found Prentice and Matheson engaged in checking the catalogue of the museum's exhibits.

"This is a job I most intensely dislike," Prentice said at once, "and Mr. Murivance must have disliked it too, since he never seems to have done it himself. Matheson, what is the number on the pot you are holding, and the description?"

"122A, sir. A section of cirrhotic liver; severe recurrent infective hepatitis with partial clinical recovery."

"A correct label at last! That is something to be thankful for. Did you want anything, Miles?"

"It is nothing much. Pounceforth has asked me to look for a little pad of notes he thinks he may have left here."

"Oh, I remember seeing him with it. It is a bright acid pink, exactly the colour Pounceforth would choose. Matheson, have you seen it?"

"No, sir, but I have not been looking for it. There are a lot of places where a little thing like that could lose itself."

"That is indisputable. Let us stop this wretched task and search for Pounceforth's pink pad. Matheson, I am leaving the higher shelves to you: I will take the three bottom ones in each row. Latimer, try the wastepaper basket and the card index."

"There is nothing in the wastepaper basket."

"There is nothing among the livers," Prentice said regretfully, foreseeing that the search might entail more exertion than he cared for. "Matheson, have you had any better luck?"

"I have found something, sir, but it isn't a pad. Perhaps you had better look at it, Dr. Prentice."

"Come and look at this, Miles," Prentice said in a high-pitched, excited voice. "Here is a peculiar thing! Matheson has found an empty syringe and needle and a rubber-capped bottle of adrenaline solution. The bottle is only half full, as you see."

"I have escaped my chores for a moment," Pounceforth said, choosing this moment to make an entry. "Have you had any success? Ah, I see you have. Latimer has found it."

"It was behind the radiator," Miles said, looking—as Pounceforth was looking—not at the pad in his hand but at the bottle in Matheson's.

"Why, what have you there, Prentice?" Pounceforth asked.

"I hardly know. Of course I know, but I cannot account for it at all. Matheson, when did you last look along that shelf?"

"I wouldn't care to say, sir, not to the day."

"Before Mr. Murivance died, Matheson?"

"Oh, yes, sir, certainly before that. I dust the hearts every week or two and it would be the first job for tomorrow morning."

"There must be some simple explanation," Pounceforth said in an easy tone.

"There must be an explanation," Prentice echoed, "but I fail to see how it could be simple."

"Latimer, how would you explain it?"

Miles seemed not to hear Pounceforth's question.

"What are we to do with these things?" Prentice asked.

"Shall I put them in the wastepaper basket, sir?"

"No, that isn't where they belong. They don't seem to belong anywhere. Perhaps I had better take them to Professor Honeychurch."

"Yes, yes, that is the best thing," Pounceforth said with an enthusiasm that seemed to be misplaced. "Don't you agree, Latimer?"

"Miles, are you quite well?" Prentice cried as Miles raised an uncertain hand to his eyes. "Matheson, bring Dr. Latimer a chair, a glass of water. What is it? Pounceforth, what is wrong with him?"

"I cannot say if you cannot. Perhaps he has read more into this little bottle and syringe than we have."

"I have not," Miles said, "I have read into it what you have, Pounceforth, no more and no less. Mr. Murivance could have used these things to kill himself. The postmortem would have revealed nothing: if he took the trouble to make the injection through one of Berringer's needle-marks there would have been no evidence. That is how I see it."

"There does not seem to be any other way," Prentice said. "Will it be necessary to tell anyone? Must the inquest be reopened? Of course there are no relations to be upset if the truth is revealed. But then, it seems so unnecessary; if Mr. Murivance went to such pains to cover up his act, it would be distinctly unkind to bring the matter into public notice."

"Yes, I agree with you there, Prentice," Pounceforth said with the appearance of grave consideration. "Latimer, how do you feel about this? We must tell Professor Honeychurch, I suppose. The decision cannot be taken just by ourselves in secret conclave, as it were."

"There is nothing secret about this conclave. Matheson is here."

"Matheson's discretion is to be relied on, Miles," Prentice said reprovingly.

"That is not what I meant. I meant that it was absurd to talk as if we were conspirators."

"I did not use that word," Pounceforth said. "Latimer has chosen it himself."

"It was the natural word to choose," said Miles with some impatience. "Of course we must tell Honeychurch. We had better tell everyone and have the thing out in the light of day. You were right, Pounceforth; it seems I must have given him the idea of doing away with himself."

"Don't say that, Miles, dear fellow! It was an error of judgement, perhaps, to say what you did to an old and failing man; but you could not possibly have foreseen what would happen."

"You are putting the kindest construction on it, Prentice. It is useless to imagine that everyone will do so. You see that Pounceforth has not."

Prentice went to Honeychurch immediately: Pounceforth also took it upon himself to spread the news and saw to it that Hilary was early informed. When Prentice left the professor's room, Hilary was already waiting to go in. Honeychurch listened with patience to his outburst but stirred uneasily in his chair at the suggestion that the whole affair might be kept secret.

"Dr. Scott, you must try to be reasonable! I do not know how I can preserve a secret that everyone already seems to know. I see no reason why the police should be told, if that is what you mean. I suppose we shall go on as we are and no more will be said of it."

"More will certainly be said of it," Hilary cried, forgetting everything in his indignation. "Pounceforth will see to that. And we shall not go on as we are; Miles will not, anyway. He has enough money to go somewhere else, and he will certainly go. It is no use arguing with him; I have tried. He thinks of himself as a species of murderer."

"That is simply morbid," Honeychurch said, pretending to a degree of coolness he did not feel.

"But there is no way of proving that it was not so, and Miles is a man who would always believe he was guilty until he is proved innocent."

"If it could be shown beyond the shadow of a doubt," Honeychurch said, as if to himself, "that Mr. Murivance did not take his own life——"

"There is no way of proving that a dead man has not had an injection of adrenaline."

"Nor is there any way of proving that he has. It is a queer way to commit suicide."

"It is not a bad way if one didn't want one's suicide suspected."

"But there was not any question of cheating an insurance company?" Honeychurch said in bewilderment.

"It was Miles who had to be cheated," Hilary said crisply. "Miles and the rest of us."

"But if that is what he wanted, would he have hidden his instruments where they were sure to be found within a few days? Would he have come here to kill himself when he might have gone home?"

"It would have been difficult to destroy the syringe and bottle anywhere. And adrenaline works very rapidly."

"But why use an undetectable method that must sooner or later be detected?" Honeychurch protested.

Hilary was silent for a moment. Then he said, reluctantly, "If he did not, there is only one alternative. Can Pounceforth be as vile as I am suggesting?"

"I don't know, Scott. Perhaps you should make it your business to find out."

Twelve days after Mr. Murivance's death, Miles Latimer was asked to call on the dead man's solicitors. When he came back to the College he went directly to the room he now occupied, off the museum gallery. When Prentice knocked and entered a few minutes later, he found the other man emptying the drawers of his desk and packing papers into a dispatch case.

"What is all this bustle, Latimer? Surely you are not leaving us?"

"I have to, Prentice. I managed to resist a moral compulsion, but an economic one has beaten me."

"What do you mean? What has happened?"

"I have lost all my money. Of course I haven't yet had any of it, so that is the wrong tense. I shall lose it all, I shall never have it. I suppose I should be thankful, because a weight has been lifted off my mind. I believe I do feel thankful, but not as much as I should."

"You have given up the legacy!" Prentice cried in astonishment.

"I have done nothing so heroic, I have only avoided litigation. It seems there is a married sister, a widow now. She and Mr. Murivance quarrelled many years ago. He thought she was satisfactorily provided for and she is not, she is nearly penniless. Mrs. Hale has made a claim and I have retired before it."

"So you are back where you were a fortnight ago."

"Yes, I have no money," Miles said, and did up the strap on his dispatch case before he added in some bitterness, "and I am not quite back where I was, because Pounceforth has my job for the next three years."

"Of course he would not give it up. Have you asked him? No, you haven't had time to do so, and you will not in any case."

"I should have liked to go on working here, Prentice. These few days have been very pleasant."

"I have felt that too. Oh dear, oh dear! I must not ask you what you are going to do."

"There would be nothing to tell you. First of all I am going to Mr. Murivance's flat. There are some odd things there that nobody will want and I would like to have something of his."

"That is a healthy sign," Prentice said, nodding his head to show approval.

"A sign of what? Of my robust conscience?"

"There need be nothing on your conscience."

Miles could not meet this assurance with the gratitude it deserved: it was necessary to escape from Prentice's good will as rapidly as possible. "Prentice, you are kinder than I deserve. Look, I will finish tidying up in here tomorrow. I would rather you told nobody about this until I have spoken to Honeychurch myself."

Prentice was a kind man but not always a discreet one, and in a few hours everybody in the building had some idea of what had happened, though Miles would have recognised his predicament in few of these distorted versions.

Miles let himself into Mr. Murivance's flat with the key the solicitors had lent him. The curtains had been left undrawn, and when he switched on the light, the blue expanse of window coldly mirrored his movements, which were hesitant and stamped with weariness. He stooped automatically to pick up the envelopes that lay neglected behind the door and laid them on a table. The clock on the mantelshelf had stopped; there was a soft layer of dust on all the furniture, and as he wandered about the small living room with its peculiar air of abandoned orderliness, he could see nothing that he wanted, nothing that would remind him of Mr. Murivance's benevolent intentions.

He looked across to the bureau; a single large book lay there. Miles opened it half idly. On the flyleaf the name "Sidney Berringer" had been written, followed by an address in Wimpole Street.

Miles turned off the light and locked the door behind him. He went down the stairs with the book under his arm. There was a straightforward task before him and he was glad to have it, though he had got nothing else from his visit.

"Good evening, Dr. Latimer. I cannot say this pleasure is unexpected, for of course your telephone call preceded you, and I have been able to look forward to our meeting."

"There was not much to look forward to. I only thought you might like to have your book back."

"To tell you the truth I had no idea Mr. Murivance had borrowed it! Sit down, Dr. Latimer, and take a cigar. You do not smoke? Oh, what you miss, what you miss! I will tell my receptionist to leave and then we can have a chat by the fire. You cannot wish to hurry out into this cold, inclement weather."

Miles sat down, less because he wished to than because there was nothing else he wanted to do more. Berringer soon returned.

"Draw your chair nearer, roast yourself if that is what you like. It is what I like, I do not hesitate to confess it. For my patients I recommend brisk walking in fresh air and so forth, but I see no reason why I should follow my own precepts. Their ill health brings them to me, my own perfect condition exempts me from the rules I impose upon them. A drink, Dr. Latimer?"

Miles accepted whisky in a crystal glass.

"Did you have a difficult time finding your way here? It is an awkward cross-country business coming from Caroline Square, I well remember Mr. Murivance saying so."

"I did not come from Caroline Square. I came directly from his flat, in Maida Vale. On the way, I only stopped to let you know I was coming."

"So you have not seen anybody since you found my book?"

"No. Why do you ask?"

Berringer sketched a meaningless gesture in the air. "I should not like people to think that I habitually lend valuable articles to my patients. Of course Mr. Murivance was not an ordinary patient."

"No, he cannot have been that. I understand you would rather I told nobody about this incident?"

"Oh, it is of no importance. I daresay you would not have mentioned it in any case."

"No, I don't think I would have. I only know one other person who cares for Roman antiquities, an acquaintance of mine, a Dr. Pounceforth. I would not have thought of telling him about the book. It is not a thing to arouse much interest."

"It is not. You are quite right, perfectly right."

"Is anything wrong, Mr. Berringer? You seem to be listening for something."

"Yes, I have just heard the last of my fellow consultants leave and I meant to have a word with him before I went home."

"I have detained you," Miles said, getting up. "I apologise——"

"There is not the slightest need for apologies, I asked you to stay! It was my own foolishness in overlooking the matter. Tomorrow will do as well. I will leave a note for him. I do regret seeming to speed the parting guest, Dr. Latimer. It is not a thing I make a habit of doing."

The two men left Berringer's suite, which was on the fourth floor. The landing was circular. A delicate balustrade outlined the well of the staircase.

"You would not think so to look at it," Berringer said in a high, hoarse tone somewhat different from his usual, mellow note, "but that beautiful balustrade is being slowly destroyed."

"Destroyed! How? Oh, I see," Miles said, approaching it. "There is dry rot in the house. Can nothing be done about it?"

"Nothing. If you go nearer you will see the uprights are almost like a sponge. Lean over a little, Dr. Latimer, but do not put your weight upon it, and you will see what I mean."

There was no need for Miles to put his weight upon the balustrade, as Berringer's firm, plump hands in the small of his back pushed him forwards and broke the uprights without any effort on his own part. After a moment, Berringer turned and ran down the stairs; on each landing he leant over to look at the motionless figure on the mosaic floor. When he was halfway down, a door behind him flew open. He wheeled round to face one of his colleagues, a gynaecologist named Pratt.

"I thought you had gone. I thought the building was empty."

"What happened? I heard the noise of wood breaking and a scream and a thud——"

"Thank God you are here, Pratt! There has been an accident. That is to say, I do not know what to say. Someone came to see me. He fell, I do not know how or why."

They began to run down the two remaining flights of stairs. Berringer was panting heavily, as the perfection of his physical condition could not stand up to the strain imposed upon it by circumstances. Pratt reached the body first.

"It is all right," he said immediately. "He is alive, Berringer. The pulse is slow but quite regular, the volume is good. You had better take a look at him yourself; this is not in my line at all. I will ring for an ambulance. No, I will not, you are not fit to stay with him. This must have been a terrible shock to you."

Berringer's distraught countenance and disordered hair gave some credence to a statement curiously wide of the mark: he preferred the truth, and for practical reasons. "No, it was not a shock at all. I will stay. I am perfectly all right, Pratt, I assure you."

"You are putting on an excellent show, but it does not deceive me. You forget that my working day is spent with women. I can detect a lie without the least difficulty, particularly a self-sacrificing one. You go and ring for the ambulance. I will stay here."

Berringer bowed to the inevitable and left the hall. When he returned, a few minutes later, he had recovered his usual bearing.

"You were right, Pratt. It was, I confess, a shock. Now I have been of some practical use, I feel a different man. I have sent to my own nursing home and they will have a bed ready for him. I had better glance at his injuries."

When he straightened up, he shook his head gravely in response to the other man's look of enquiry.

"It is better than we might have hoped, I mean than we might have feared. I think it is only his right femur that is gone. He has fractured his wrist and some ribs on that side too, but that is nothing. His pelvis seems to be sound, and there is no obvious depressed fracture of the skull, but that is not to say there is nothing at all. By a miracle he seems to have escaped without breaking his back. Will you wait here with him while I go back to my rooms? I want to fetch a blanket; and there are some X-ray films I can take in the ambulance with me to the nursing home. It is an ill wind, Pratt."

"The good in this case hardly seems commensurate with the ill," Pratt said.

"Mr. Berringer will put the leg in extension himself when they come out of the theatre; he has plastered the wrist and strapped the ribs. The X rays show no fracture of the skull, either at the base or in the vault. You will sit by the patient's bed until you are relieved. You will take his pulse at half-hourly intervals. If the patient regains consciousness, you will ring the bell at once to let me know."

"Yes, Sister."

"Patients with severe concussion," Sister said, busying her hands with chrysanthemums in a great vase, "are sometimes very excitable when they come round. Some of these flowers are dead already, Nurse. It is necessary to keep them quiet with suitable drugs; the patients, that is to say. Mr. Berringer has ordered hyoscine. There is a syringe loaded with the correct dose on the trolley. You will not give it without consulting me. I think all these should be thrown out before you go off duty. They will not last until morning."

"No, Sister. Yes, Sister. No, Sister."

"I have bewildered you," the sister said with a sudden lightness that produced an answering rise of spirits in her nurse. "That was not what I intended. Forget about the flowers and concentrate upon the patient. He will have what is called a retrograde amnesia when he comes round. He will remember things that happened to him a few days before the accident, even a few hours, but he will not remember the accident itself or the events leading up to it.

Later he will remember more and more. Dr. Latimer is very lucky to be alive."

"Will he be all right, Sister?"

"Try not to ask foolish questions, Nurse. No patient with a head injury can be said to be all right for at least three weeks."

"Then, he might die, Sister."

"Well, of course he might. That is what I mean. But I don't myself think he will, though you must certainly not tell anyone I said so." She abandoned the chrysanthemums herself as being past hope, unlike her patient, and led her nurse into the room set aside for Miles. "Here are the pictures of his broken leg. Put them on the locker; we can put the other plates there when the radiographer sends them up."

"But these are dry already, Sister."

"Yes, Mr. Berringer took them in his own consulting rooms while they were waiting for the ambulance. You see, there is an oblique fracture of the right femur. Mr. Berringer will straighten the bones by strapping the leg to a Thomas splint and attaching weights and pulleys. He will probably have more X rays taken tomorrow to see whether the fragments are in good alignment."

But when Sister suggested that he might fill up the necessary form that night so that the radiographer could come to the bedside in the morning, Berringer shook his head. "We will leave it for a few days. There was not much displacement and I think the leg is nearly straight now. The weights will do the rest. I don't want Dr. Latimer disturbed. I would like to be told directly he regains consciousness. I wish him to be discouraged from talking. Give him the hyoscine I have ordered as often as you find it necessary to keep him really quiet."

"I have nursed head injury cases for you before, Mr. Berringer."

"Yes, Sister, I know. You must forgive me. Put my rudeness down to nervous strain. I did not know this man at all, but he went out of his way to do me a little kindness, and as things turned out he might have met his death doing it, might even now meet it, I fear. He found a book someone had borrowed from me, and returned it. It was not of any particular value, just a small volume of poetry, but it was kind of him to bring it back. And now this dreadful thing has happened and I am more upset than I would have believed possible. Good night."

As soon as he left, Sister turned to the mirror in her office, patted her hair, and spoke over her shoulder. "The essence of a good doctor is his human sympathy, Nurse. You saw for yourself how Mr. Berringer was affected. Dr. Latimer could not be in better hands."

"I am sure he could not, Sister."

Between Berkhamsted and Tring, small hills rise in a trite and orderly sequence and are covered with bracken. By November the bracken is parched and brown. The neat, pointed shoes of a plump walker on one particular night raised formidable creaks and splutters; his attempts to move more quietly produced a slow, discursive series of explosions underfoot as time and again he broke the desiccated fronds. His goal seemed to be an isolated group of trees, hardly large enough to be called a wood; but as he approached it his path swerved wider and wider in a contradictory aversion that might or might not have been against his will. He came to a noisy stop on a hillock about twenty yards away from the spinney and watched it covertly as if he thought some other might be watching him.

Nobody was, but he had to pay a price for illegal, not to say immoral, behaviour; he stood on a pillory of his own choosing, and here discovered that the murderer does not always return to the scene of his crime. He could not do this, though he had got so near it.

Capriciously, the wind rose and blew over the face of the half moon till the last cloud drew away, and the plump man came off his hillock in a hurry, feeling himself more conspicuous even than before. This time, he walked resolutely to the north, parallel with the long side of the spinney. The ground became frighteningly uneven and was scarred with trenches, made hazardous by wooden pegs thrust into holes with indistinguishable letters painted on them. At last, stretching away to the west until the bushes on the edge of the spinney defined a margin was a smooth rectangular floor over which danced young women and a variety of birds and fishes snared in a net of stone and wholly unresistant to his encroaching tread. His shadow fell over the mosaic and was soon mixed with other shadows as he came nearer to the trees.

He never reached them but stopped again dead in his tracks, shaking his head obstinately as if he were caught on the wrong side in an argument. Then he glanced at his watch, tapped his way back over the floor of this Roman villa, crossed the wide strip of common between the site and the road, and climbed into the driving seat of his car. But he did not drive off immediately. He sat at the wheel, smoking, and sometimes raised his eyes to a signpost a few yards ahead with the single word "Throckleford" painted on the crossbar. In the intermittent moonlight, his incurably romantic eye saw that in outline a signpost resembles a scaffold. When this idea occurred to him, he threw his cigarette out of the window and drove off towards the village.

"A girl like you," he said to the barmaid in Throckleford's larger public house, "must find a place like this rather a dead end?"

He was always heavy-handed with women and once had been fatally so, but he had no rivals; the bar was not empty, but there was no one else there with a pearl tiepin, or even a tie so beautifully folded under so smooth a collar. It was a pity that he was bald and fat and that his hands were white and soft. The barmaid's reading had told her that men's hands should be brown and strong, forbearing to mention that skilful deployment is a good substitute for mere strength.

"Yes, it's certainly dull," she acceded with caution, handing him his gin.

"You will have one with me?"

In the event, she accepted two with protests that were not more than halfhearted.

"The dig," he began awkwardly. "The Roman remains up the road——"

She interpreted this as amorous in intent and shook her head with emphasis. "Creepy. And too cold by a long way at this time of year."

It had not been too cold two months before, for there had been a St. Martin's summer and the wood had been warm and dry. On the other side of the bushes spades might even then have been striking against stone, bosoms more chaste may well have been exposed to eyes less lecherous than his.

"Nobody is digging there now," he remarked pointlessly, thinking of the spade and the sacking in the back of his car.

"Oh, no," she readily agreed. "They won't be back till March, they said. It livens things up a bit when they come."

"It must do," he said. His own presence had had a different effect. "So they won't be back for a good while yet?"

"Nobody goes up there in winter. It might almost be haunted, the way people don't go up there."

"Do you know any of the archaeologists—any of the diggers?" he awkwardly demanded, sipping his gin with distaste.

"Only to pass the time of day. They mostly drop in here after lunch. But they're only here at weekends, you know. Amateurs, they call themselves, and bring their wives with them."

"Did you ever meet a chap called Pounceforth?" He brought out the name at last.

"Oh, *him!*" she said, and needed to say no more. At any rate he heard no more, his fears having reached confirmation so simply and with such completeness. He paid for the drinks and said his goodnight absently. He was not a good actor: one man cannot be all things.

V

The following morning, Professor Honeychurch arrived at the College with his usual sense of homecoming. He found his secretary looking pale and alarmed, and detected in the anteroom a faint odour of Worth's Je Reviens, a perfume Kate Cardew did not use.

"There is someone to see you, a Mr. Berringer. He says that Dr. Latimer has had an accident, has been badly hurt, is in a nursing home."

Honeychurch moved past her, into his room. Sidney Berringer rose from his chair and extended a hand with a card; then, with extreme neatness, retrieved the card in order to shake Honeychurch's hand, bowing over it his generously silvered head.

"Mr. Berringer, it is good of you to come. What has happened to Dr. Latimer?"

"Professor Honeychurch, I rejoice to have the opportunity of meeting you; I mean, I would rejoice in other circumstances. As it is——"

"As it is, we must forget our mutual rejoicings and share this dreadful news. Tell me what has happened. Is it serious, is it dangerous?"

"It is both."

"Sit down, please. Kate, come in and shut the door, and sit down too, my dear."

"I don't know how I dare come with such tidings," Berringer said with a cheerfulness he altogether failed to disguise: fortunately his audience put it down to deficient sensibility and nothing worse. "Mr. Murivance left my rooms and came here to die. Now Dr. Latimer has met with an accident before he was even out of the building. Soon none of your staff will dare set foot in the place."

"How did it happen?" Honeychurch asked patiently, seeing that impatience would bring the truth out no sooner.

"He was admiring the balustrade on our staircase. It is William Kent's work, very fine, but in poor condition; dangerous condition, as the event proved. I warned him not to let his weight rest upon it. I can only think he did not hear me. He has recovered consciousness now; he has broken a leg, a wrist, some ribs. He is quite incoherent and very noisy. We have had to keep him heavily drugged during the night. I have not yet seen him this morning; if you would like to come with me, I can drive you there at once."

"This will be Mr. Roberts," Kate said mechanically, hearing footsteps and a knock on the door. She did not get up, suspecting that she could not.

"Come in, William. You had better hear the news at once."

"This is a bad thing," Roberts said when he had heard Berringer's story. "What was he doing in your consulting rooms, Berringer?"

"He returned a book to me that Mr. Murivance borrowed some weeks ago. Latimer found it among his personal effects. It makes it worse that this should have happened while he was doing me a kindness. I cannot forgive myself for drawing his attention to the balustrade."

"Dr. Prentice," Kate said, opening the door herself this time.

Roberts and Honeychurch exchanged glances of caution, but Berringer did not know Prentice and seemed to have an overwhelming desire to unburden himself of his tale of woe.

Prentice changed colour and sat down. "I foresaw this. I believe I knew it would happen. It was too much for him."

"It would be too much for anyone to fall fifty feet without sustaining an injury," Roberts said hastily.

"That is not what I meant, Roberts, you know it is not. I mean this talk that has been going around, these malicious rumours. That is what has done it. So much talk of self-destruction, so much morbid suggestion, and losing his money on top of everything!"

"You think Dr. Latimer attempted to kill himself?" Berringer said with unaffected astonishment. "Why has there been so much talk of suicide?"

"There has been a suggestion about Mr. Murivance," Prentice told him. "A bottle of adrenaline and a syringe was found in the museum. Pounceforth took it upon himself to spread a rumour—it doesn't matter what rumour he spread."

"No, it doesn't matter, Prentice," Honeychurch said quickly, "since Mr. Berringer hardly knows Latimer and doesn't know Pounceforth at all. It would be better if there were no suggestions about Miles."

"But certainly it must be thought of," Berringer said. "It is not the sort of notion to be dismissed out of hand. This seemed on the face of it a curious accident. I had wondered if our friend might have had a dizzy spell, a syncope, as he stood there. But if his action was intentional, perhaps I need not blame myself so much."

"I must blame myself instead," Prentice said with an insistence that seemed at odds with the emotion he meant to evoke. "I should have taken it upon myself to watch over him a little in those difficult days."

"Mr. Berringer," Honeychurch said with a touch of acerbity, "I will not keep you waiting. Is your car here?"

"It is at the door."

"Then, if you will precede me? I must make some simple arrangements. William, a word with you."

"Prentice has already gone," Roberts said as Berringer closed the door. "In less than ten minutes his feelings of guilt will be the property of the whole College. He is much less reticent than Miles."

"Miles was obviously not reticent enough."

"It was no use Miles's being reticent. His feelings were publicised for him by Pounceforth and some others. I include myself, by the way."

"William, is it possible he might have done this thing? Are you going to be wise after the event?"

"I was wise long before, Fabian, even before Prentice. Two weeks ago, when Scott and Miss Cardew became engaged and he had no money, Latimer told me he had thought of it. Naturally I assumed he was speaking lightly."

"Scott and Miss Cardew are no longer engaged," Honeychurch pointed out, and suddenly remembered the girl's silent presence; she seemed not to have heard, sitting there with a white face and a withdrawn, intent look.

"But Scott's loss cannot be thought of as Latimer's gain," Roberts said, ignoring her still. "And there was Mr. Murivance and the legacy and settling down happily to the work he wanted to do, only to have it all snatched away.

And Pounceforth's slanders may have done their share. It might have been enough."

"I believe it was," Honeychurch said wretchedly. "I wonder how Pounceforth will take the news?"

"Oh, he is not a truly imaginative man, much less so than Latimer. It is just as well he isn't, because the reputation of the College would hardly stand three suicides, or even one suicide and two attempts. Your efforts to build up a happy working community here must have failed, Fabian."

"We should not keep Berringer waiting so long. It is rude of me to keep him waiting at all. Kate, there are messages I must leave——"

"Do not leave them with Miss Cardew," Roberts said, taking in the situation belatedly but with some insight. "The beadle will do all you need. There is not as much as you think."

"William, in another person your assurance would be intolerable."

"That is only a kind way of saying it is intolerable in me."

Berringer drove Honeychurch through damp and misty streets towards St. John's Wood. He turned into a cul-de-sac and through a pair of wrought-iron gates. The drive led to a substantial Victorian house standing in a garden of dripping shrubs and sodden lawns. Inside, all was warm, spacious, and luxurious without ostentation. A lift had been installed; they ascended. Berringer indicated a door, and Honeychurch passed through it while Berringer called the sister to his side.

"There is more to this than meets the eye, Sister," he

said in a low, rapid tone. "It looks as if our patient here was trying to commit suicide. He has been depressed about money and other things too, I don't know exactly what. At any rate, his friends were not as surprised by his fall as I was, and that was the reason."

"It need not make any difference to his nursing."

"Well, no, I suppose it need not. But you will have to keep an eye on him. He may require protecting from himself."

"He can hardly make a further attempt as things are now, Mr. Berringer."

"You reassure me, Sister. As usual, your common sense must counterbalance my weather-vane temperament."

"I know you do not know what you would do without me, if that is what you mean."

"You have rare insight, Sister. That comes of being a woman."

"I am easily flattered, Mr. Berringer, which perhaps comes from the same source."

"What I wanted to convey," he said, put out more than a little by this woman's perspicacity, "and mind you, I trust to your good sense to put the correct interpretation upon my words—was only that our patient's mental state is probably peculiar. He may have ideas that seem bizarre; he may even have delusions, ideas of persecution and so forth."

"Do you mean to report this to the police, Mr. Berringer?"

"I think not, Sister. There is no need to add a further load to a soul already sinking under its burden."

"Is that what the police would do? I always understood they were invaluable on such an occasion."

"On some occasions, perhaps, but not precisely this one," Berringer said with a slight frown.

They joined Honeychurch in the quiet gloom of the room allotted to Miles. He was asleep, his leg raised at an angle above the bed and suspended from a beam. A nurse sat by the window, and rose as they came in.

"Sit down, sit down, Nurse! A few minutes off your feet will do you no harm. Poor young things, how sadly we drive them!"

Sister looked at the nurse as if seeing her for the first time and not seeing any sign of her having been treated in the way Berringer suggested. The nurse, catching Sister's eye, remained standing.

"The healing powers of sleep are not to be underestimated, Professor Honeychurch," Berringer remarked largely.

"I see they are not. I have been looking at your prescription sheet, Mr. Berringer. You believe in large doses of hyoscine for head injuries?"

"Rest, rest for the perturbed spirit. Rest is what it craves!"

"And you believe in ministering to the craving? You would give rest unlimited?"

"Well, not unlimited, of course—that would be death, wouldn't it? That is something quite different."

"I wish the difference were more strongly marked," Honeychurch said, bending over the bed to catch the elusive evidence of breathing.

"Latimer was very excited when he came round. He vomited repeatedly, complained of headache, began to throw himself about. Further injury must be prevented, and this is the only way to do it."

"I defer to your judgement. I have had very little experience of head injuries. May I come again?"

"I believe I may say yes. It is not advisable for him to have frequent visitors; it would be unwise to rouse him or to try to recall unhappy circumstances to him while his soul prefers oblivion."

"It is so satisfactory to hear that his soul is in good hands," Honeychurch said. "It is not every surgeon who caters for the soul's preferences."

"A patient is a whole, Professor Honeychurch. We treat more than the bare bones. We give the medicine, but God heals the sick."

"So I believe; but I continue to give the medicine, and I see that you do too, Berringer."

"Hilary, have you seen Miles?"

"Not yet, Kate. He isn't allowed casual visitors. I don't feel like a casual visitor, but they refused to let me in."

"Shall we go into the square? There is a seat under the holly tree that is nearly dry, and it is not as cold as it was earlier."

"It is cold enough and it is time for lunch," Hilary said decidedly. "Have you had any lunch?"

"I have had something. Have you?"

"No. Let's go into the square."

He spread his raincoat on the seat, which was far from dry, after all.

"Did you get any more news?" she asked at last with some hesitation.

"He knows who he is, and where he is, and that he has had a fall. The sister is a competent woman who would not make things out better or worse than they really are. I believe she knows that it was not simply an accident."

"Everybody thinks they know that, but only Miles can really know. I am ashamed of myself, Hilary. I should never have listened to Pounceforth's nonsense; or I should have listened and recognised that the whole thing was a lie."

"It *was* a lie," he said with vehemence. "It was an acted lie, not just a spoken one, and I intend to prove it. That shouldn't be impossible."

"You cannot alter what has already been done."

"I might prevent its being done again."

"You think," she said, searching her handbag intently for nothing in particular, "you think he might try again, Hilary?"

"I don't know. How could I know? What did he feel like before he did it, and will he feel differently when he remembers? I cannot answer those questions any more than you can."

"Take me to see him when they let you go, Hilary! I would rather not try now; I have too much pride to risk being called a casual visitor."

"Kate, I wonder——"

"Try not to. There is nothing to wonder about."

"Are you thinking what it must have been like to be Zuleika Dobson?"

She looked up at him with grateful affection and his heart sank, knowing their engagement would never be renewed, though their friendship had been. "Yes, that is what I was thinking. You are remarkably sensitive, Hilary."

"Sensitivity is a quality I can dispense with if I am to prove that Pounceforth did what I think he did," Hilary said, covering his discomfort as well as he could. "I shall cultivate a hide as tough as his. It is in a good cause."

After lunch he went back to the College and found

Pounceforth sitting at his desk with his head between his hands.

"Scott, I believe I shall leave you in charge this afternoon. I have the beginnings of a migraine and the sensible thing would be to go home to bed. I don't think there is any useful work in me today."

"There is no useful work in me, either. I won't pretend I am going to stay here, Pounceforth. There is not much to be done and what there is will keep."

Pounceforth did not stay to argue, foreseeing that argument would only result in a further loss of face. Hilary waited until he was gone and then went down to the museum.

"Matheson, can I ask you a question? I would rather nobody knew that I have asked it. How often is the museum left unattended during the day?"

"It isn't left at all, sir. Mr. Murivance preferred it not to be left. Of course, things have been different since he died, and will be until someone comes to take his place."

"Yes, that is what I mean. In the last ten days or so it might just have been possible for someone to slip in when neither you nor Dr. Prentice was about. Can you think of a time when it might have been left as long as half an hour?"

"Oh, several times, sir. Not once but often, I'm sorry to say. We have taken to locking the door during the lunch hour, but there is always the odd time when Dr. Prentice has been lecturing downstairs and I have gone to fetch specimens and we have thought it wrong to shut people out when they might have come a long way to work here."

"Could anyone have found out when you were both likely to be away?"

"Dr. Prentice's lectures are announced on the board in the hall, sir. My own movements are not of so much interest. If somebody wanted to be alone in here it would be easy enough to wait till I was out of the way. What was it you had in mind, sir?"

Hilary looked sharply at this sensible, obliging little man.

"I believe you know, Matheson, without my telling you."

"Of course I do, sir. And I remember something that seemed queer to me though I didn't think much of it at the time. There was dust, quite a lot of dust on the shelves where the heart specimens are, but there wasn't much on the syringe or the bottle when I found them. It was a week then since the old gentleman died. You will know what to make of that. I wonder if there were fingerprints on that syringe?"

"I'm sure there were not," Hilary said decidedly. "You and I are not the only people who read detective stories. I wonder if we are being morbidly imaginative."

"Probably, sir, but in the midst of life, as the saying goes. It is really not so surprising when you think of the skeleton, too. It didn't need Dr. Latimer to point out that that was a sinister business."

"Do you know, it never seemed sinister to me? I simply took it at its face value, and I must say I think Mr. Murivance did too. Could there really be anything to it?"

They stood before the skeleton.

"We still don't know who sent her," Hilary said thoughtfully. "Could it matter, do you think?"

"You cannot go leaving stones unturned, sir, if you want to get to the bottom of this business."

"Where do you think she comes from?"

"Well, sir, that's not quite the same thing as asking who sent her. I should guess she came from Trimble's at some time or other; but of course that may have been years ago."

Hilary saw Mr. Trimble and his order book and returned to the College with both of them about dusk. He did not bother to conceal his excitement, since he saw no one on his way to Honeychurch's room.

"Come in, Dr. Scott. I am happily unoccupied just now. Miss Cardew is looking for some papers for me to sign and there is nothing for me to do until she comes back."

"Pounceforth sent the skeleton to Mr. Murivance," Hilary said. "That is, Pounceforth bought a skeleton a month ago and Mr. Murivance received one a week later; both were female. I think they must have been the same."

"Are you sure of this, Scott? How did you find out?"

Hilary told him, calming himself sufficiently to produce the appearance of a reliable informant. Honeychurch became agitated in his turn. Since he was a larger man than Hilary, his agitation assumed greater dimensions; the room was soon filled with his perturbation.

"This is worse than I ever guessed. It is far too bad for us to hedge and hint about. It will have to come out into the open."

"We cannot prove Pounceforth sent it."

"Do we need proof? The crime we think Pounceforth has committed is hardly one that a jury could try or a judge punish."

"It is not a crime at all," Hilary pointed out. "There is no law prohibiting people from sending skeletons about the country. Nobody would think such a law was needed.

Besides, there is something else Pounceforth might have done, and that is not a crime either." He told Honeychurch of his conversation with the museum attendant.

"Matheson is an observant fellow," Honeychurch said musingly, "and we have always found him reliable. I suppose there *might* be a law to prevent a man creating false evidence of another man's having committed suicide; it seems unlikely. Pounceforth's activities are certainly extraordinary to a degree! What can have prompted them?"

"They were directed against Miles," Hilary said with some impatience. "That much is clear enough."

"I cannot be as certain of that as you are, I fear. Say that Pounceforth sent Murivance the skeleton; he could never have anticipated that Miles would make that unfortunate remark, let alone that Murivance would die so soon afterwards. If he wanted Murivance to die, he might have gone about it more directly, and if he only meant to discomfort Miles, then the death of Murivance seems a drastic way of gaining a small end. It would be something new to murder two men through their own susceptibility to suggestion, and it is not the sort of thing that would occur to Pounceforth. He is not at all a subtle person, do you think? Besides, what good would either death have done him? He has already stepped into Miles's shoes, and I don't know that he ever wished to step into Murivance's. This is all nonsense; there is no sense in the business from beginning to end."

"There is some sense in the simple facts at least. Prove to Miles that Murivance did not kill himself, and Miles would not need to kill himself, either."

"You think he will try again, Scott, if he recovers?"

"Nothing has changed since he tried before," Hilary said

bitterly. "Things do not change of their own accord. Won't you come down and see Mr. Trimble, sir?"

"What do you mean to do, exactly?"

"He has brought along the man who articulated Pounceforth's skeleton. They think that he will recognise her if she is the right one."

A few minutes later, Honeychurch and Scott, and Trimble and his assistant, went into the museum looking peculiarly guilty, as if they were involved in some shameful conspiracy. Pounceforth was known to be out of the building, but his incorporeal presence oppressed Hilary and Honeychurch and intimidated the innocent Trimble, though he could not say why. Of them all, only the technician seemed cheerful, and this was in part because his expert services had been called for and in part because it looked as if they would be paid for also. Matheson opened the door and led them to the skeleton.

"That is the one," the man said immediately.

"You are quite sure?" Honeychurch asked. "There is no doubt at all in your mind? We don't want to hurry you or have you say what you think would please us."

"How should I know what would please you? I know my own work when I see it. Look at that carpus: look at the superior radioulnar joint. Nobody else does that joint as well as I do. This is a skeleton I articulated myself, the one you saw in the order book. I recognise her as I would recognise my own child in the street."

"Thank you, thank you," Honeychurch cried, preferring not to dwell too long on this image. "You have been a great help. Mr. Trimble; thank you for letting us have his aid. If I might add something a little more tangible in the way of gratitude——"

A note changed hands.

"What are all these people doing here?" Prentice said. "Why are they looking at the skeleton, Professor Honeychurch?"

"Why, Prentice, we were not expecting you," Honeychurch remarked blandly but disingenuously, as Hilary had earlier told him that Prentice would be lecturing to postgraduates at this hour.

"There is no reason why you should have," Prentice said, staring a little longer at his unexpected visitors than was quite polite. "Only five of my postgraduates turned up, perhaps because of the weather, and I brought them up here to look at some pots, since a formal lecture would be out of place. Gentlemen," he turned to his five embarrassed satellites, "the material you wish to examine is arranged on the shelves nearest the fireplace. Mr. Trimble, to what do I owe this pleasure?"

"You know Mr. Trimble?"

"Most certainly I do, Professor Honeychurch. He and Mr. Murivance and myself were well acquainted."

"Dr. Scott was showing us some of your splendid collection," Mr. Trimble said, showing himself not altogether deficient of resource though incapable of the highest flights of imagination. "I paused to admire this lady, and now I hear she comes from our own workshops."

"Does she really?" Prentice said with cheerful amazement. "Well, I might have guessed it, if I had only given the matter a little thought. Why didn't I think of it? Why didn't Murivance think of it and come to you?"

Mr. Trimble remained silent, not being able to think of any good reason why Mr. Murivance should not have done what in fact he had done.

"And now you will be able to tell us who sent her here, and there will be no more surmising! I wish Mr. Murivance had lived to see this day. It was only a little thing, but it piqued his curiosity."

"It will continue to pique ours," Honeychurch said hastily. "I have asked Mr. Trimble the name of the purchaser and he prefers not to tell us. There is an etiquette in these matters and it would hardly be fair of us to press him to a disclosure."

"I am not at all sure that that was the right thing to say," he remarked to Hilary a little later, when they were alone.

"Is it so unnerving to discover that one is a competent liar?"

"I fear there was no lying involved, and it seems rather unkind to Mr. Trimble to have told the truth at such a moment. Have you seen Miles?"

"Not yet. They wouldn't let me."

"There is so little we can do," Honeychurch said despondently; they were back in his room, and possibly his feeling of helplessness was increased by old association. "Perhaps my solicitors could arrange an endowment to cover his work in such a way that he would never find out where the money came from."

"He would guess. And he would guess that it was done to prevent his trying to take his life again. He would feel as if he had extorted money from you by a threat."

"But there are other reasons for giving him money. His work is important, and he would do it well."

Hilary shook his head.

"That is not the reason he would find."

"You know him better than I do," Honeychurch said,

and was silent, looking at the dying embers of his fire; it hardly seemed to be worth replenishing. He said heavily, "So Pounceforth's skeleton is Mr. Murivance's skeleton, and Pounceforth achieves the status of a murderer by his own definition. *He* reminded Murivance that death was his inevitable portion and Murivance is dead. I find I am continually wrong in my estimate of other men's characters: I would not have thought Mr. Murivance either so obliging or so acutely sensitive. I would have thought it a coincidence, if Pounceforth had not tried to teach us otherwise. And he tried so hard: that makes it seem improbable to me that he had any major part in the affair."

"If Mr. Murivance's death were not just a coincidence? If Pounceforth were in fact a murderer?"

"There are no poisons unknown to science, I hope."

"There is adrenaline," Hilary said, "and that is undetectable. We know there is adrenaline, because Pounceforth led us to it."

"That is against his having used it," Honeychurch suggested.

"We could never prove that he had used it," Hilary said stubbornly, "and we could never prove that Mr. Murivance did not."

Honeychurch unlocked a drawer in his desk and took out the syringe and the rubber-capped bottle that Matheson had found.

"Enough has been taken out of this bottle to kill a man if it were injected quickly. Of course any injection against a person's will would have to be made quickly. I don't think it could be made at all."

"A preliminary stunning with a light blow?" Hilary said with relish.

"There was no evidence," Honeychurch said, and added, "No, the injection cannot have been made, now I come to think of it; there was no needle mark except the six Berringer accounted for. So Pounceforth would have had a difficult task: to undress a conscious victim, to inject the adrenaline through a previous puncture site, to dress him again. All this without making a sound; there were people in the building that night and they heard nothing. It isn't possible, Scott."

Hilary said dejectedly, "I see it isn't. I was a fool ever to entertain such an idea. And suicide is equally impossible, because nobody could inject that fatal dose of adrenaline into his own shoulder, dress himself again, and hide away the syringe. Adrenaline would kill almost instantaneously."

"So it would! Why didn't I think of that before?" Honeychurch said, striking his fist upon the desk. "He cannot have been murdered, he cannot have committed suicide; ergo, he must have died a natural death. We are back where we were. Pounceforth is a blackguard, but he is not an absolute villain."

"It seems a very fine distinction!"

"So fine that it may not be valid at all. But at least you can prove to Miles that he didn't drive poor Murivance to his death, and that is what you wanted."

"Will you speak to Pounceforth, Professor Honeychurch?"

"I will think about it. Something requires saying, but I am not sure yet what it is. Certainly he must not come out of this thing without some punishment."

"He should resign; he should hand Miles's job back to him."

"His conscience might tell him that."

"His conscience is such an elastic member," Hilary pointed out. "It seems to permit things outside the usual range. I don't suppose it will turn fastidious for our convenience."

"It may require a little guidance," Honeychurch said with some dignity, "and I shall give it. That is a thing I feel myself well able to do."

VI

Miles passed in and out of sleep, an uneasy sleep threaded by nightmares: the nightmares were diversely peopled, but all tended to the same conclusion, and he woke crying out from the imagined terror of a fall. The real world wavered and swam before his eyes; sickness and headache pounced on his moments of wakefulness until hyoscine thrust him back into his merciless recurrent dreams. Through four days and nights he lived in a territory mapped out by fear and bounded by annihilation. On the fifth morning there was less pain and no nausea. He turned his head with experienced caution and the movement failed to hurt or sicken. His mouth was dry; he moistened his lips and asked for a drink. The sounds he made were muffled and remote to his own ears. He shaped the words again, and this time the nurse who sat by his bed turned sharply towards him with an expression he could not understand.

Miles said, "You look as if you were afraid of something. What is there to be afraid of?"

"This is the first time you have woken up quietly. I thought you might have taken a turn for the worse. Oh, I shouldn't have said that!"

"I believe I have taken a turn for the better. I must have, if I can talk sensibly. Am I talking sensibly?"

She got up and smoothed her apron. "More sensibly

than you have done. You have said some very odd things since you came here; shouted them, rather."

"Is there water in that feeding cup?"

"Lemon juice." She helped him to drink it.

"That is what I wanted! What is this place? How long have I been here?"

"Four days; it is a nursing home. I am not allowed to tell you any more. Perhaps I should not have told you that much."

"There are some things even a patient has a right to know," he said mildly. "What day of the week is it?"

"Saturday."

"Then, tomorrow is Sunday and I can rest all day. No, that's absurd. I can rest for a long time now. Is my leg broken?"

"Yes, and your wrist, and some ribs."

"They don't hurt much. I always thought a fracture would be unbearably painful. My wrist aches, but the leg feels comfortable. It will take weeks to mend, months even. I think I must have died and this must be heaven."

"I will go and tell Sister you are better."

"Nurse says your condition has improved, Dr. Latimer. I am glad to hear it."

The sister had a long brown face with inconsiderable eyes and a sardonic mouth. She took a sheaf of notes from a board on the wall and wrote something on them in a bold script.

"Has anyone been to see me?"

"Far too many people. I have had to spend a fair part of my working day fending them off. You will be able to have visitors now, only one a day at first, and not for more than a few minutes at a time. And you must not talk about things that excite you."

"I cannot think of anything that would excite me now; I have never felt so calm in my life. I don't even want to know what happened to me, how I fell, I mean. Who is looking after me?"

"Mr. Sidney Berringer: this is his nursing home. You are in good hands."

"I will take your word for it, Sister. He is only a name to me."

"It will all come back to him in time," Sister said, closing the door behind her. "He mustn't be left alone today. We cannot expect him to make rapid progress, and he may even get worse again before he gets better."

Kate and Hilary came together that afternoon; it was decided that Kate should spend a few minutes with Miles while Hilary drank tea with Sister in her sitting room.

"Does he know what happened?" Hilary asked her as soon as they were alone.

"He knows the effect," Sister said guardedly. "He has asked no questions, and if he does they will be evaded. Mr. Berringer doesn't want him to be reminded too soon."

"Kate will not remind him. There is a lot to be done before he can be allowed to remember."

"I am sure Miss Cardew will say nothing to upset him. If I were not sure, I would not have allowed her to go to him."

"It is odd how Miles brings out the best in people. It is as if his caring so little about himself encouraged others to supply the deficiency."

"I don't think suicide is the act of a man who cares too

little about himself. It might be the result of caring too much."

"Who has said anything to you about suicide?" Hilary said with a sense of outrage. "What gave you such an idea?"

"It is only a suspicion, and I should not have mentioned it. Mr. Berringer led me to suppose that the suspicion derived from Dr. Latimer's friends, and I counted you among them."

Hilary sat back in his chair. Sister poured tea from a silver teapot and handed him a cup in silence. He refused milk and sugar, and at last said carefully, "I don't see why Berringer should have mentioned it either. Such things are not meant for general publication. It might do considerable harm."

"Mr. Berringer was anxious that no further harm should be done. It is only fair to tell you as much, even if it pains you. I pointed out that opportunities would scarcely be forthcoming in this place and in Dr. Latimer's present state, but Mr. Berringer seemed to be carried away by his feelings. He also made it clear that we must not be surprised if our patient exhibited some curious mental aberrations when he recovered. We shall not be surprised, of course, because experience has taught us what to expect of head injuries."

"Mr. Berringer's celebrated tact seems to have deserted him!"

"I don't wish to complain. I am complaining, though; it is very disloyal of me. The incident left its mark, and I cannot quite erase it. Dr. Scott, I must trust you to be discreet although I haven't been so myself. We had better forget this conversation."

"It will not be easy to forget it," Hilary said. "You have

told me yourself you cannot forget another conversation, and there seems to be no better reason for remembering that."

"Of course, Mr. Berringer was upset," she said thoughtfully. "It was a dreadful thing to see happen before his own eyes to a man who had just done him a little service."

"Bringing him back his book, you mean? Was it something very important, so that he was especially glad to have it, and especially disturbed by what happened?"

"A small volume of poetry, he said, not of any value."

"Perhaps he had forgotten about it, or given it up for lost. It is always a heartening experience to get something back when you have given it up for lost."

"I only hope that is how Dr. Latimer will feel about his life," she said.

"You look thinner, Miles."

"I have eaten nothing for four days, or so they tell me. They don't tell me much, because I am not allowed to get excited; but do you know I find it rather exciting that they are so mysterious about everything? I keep wondering what can have happened that needs to be kept such a secret. Have I done something shocking, Kate?"

It seemed to Kate that the question was seriously asked in spite of its seeming flippancy, and because she would not answer it seriously she did not answer it at all; she only smiled, and this smile that warmed and softened her composed, intelligent face warmed Miles, also. He retreated precipitately from its radiance, thinking his physical hurt was enough to bear for the time being. In a voice colder than he intended, he asked why Hilary had not come.

"He has!" she said, surprised. "But only one of us could come in and he let me. He will come tomorrow instead."

He hid his resurgent rebellious delight by turning his head away, and said over his shoulder, "I wanted Hilary to do something for me."

"Tell me what it is," she suggested. "I can give your message to him."

"They say I mustn't read yet, and I must; or, rather, someone must read to me. I have only three years to do my work and I may be here for months. I shall have to get the preliminary reading done and the investigation planned."

Kate said slowly, so slowly that he turned back to look at her, "You should not think of it yet. Wait a few weeks at least. Mr. Berringer says you need all the rest you can get."

"But how can I rest?" he asked patiently, as if he were explaining his affairs to a child. "I can see my timetable going to pieces. Weeks will go by and nothing will be done. That worries me far more than the work would do; surely you see that, Kate?"

Not knowing what to say, she looked towards the door, perhaps even hoping that Hilary would come and rescue her from this impossible situation.

"If you will just ask Prentice to let you have the books; he knows which ones I want."

"In a week or two, Miles," she said rapidly. "Don't try to rush things."

"If you are too busy," he said, his face suddenly bleak, "then it doesn't matter. I am sorry, Kate, I did not mean to be so selfish. I have so much time on my hands now that it is difficult to realise everyone is not so lucky."

"It is I who have been selfish," she said. "I will see Prentice and we will arrange something."

Miles saw that there was something wrong; he lay staring at the window; a few damp leaves flapped against the glass, adhered for a moment and were sucked off by the returning wind.

"Kate, I believe there is something I have forgotten that I should hate to know if I could remember it. And yet I want to remember it; whatever it is, it couldn't be worse than this uncertainty. If you know what I mean, will you tell me?"

Kate said nothing, and did not realise how clearly her expression spoke.

"Then, it is something I won't like," he said half to himself, "something you think it is better for me not to know."

"There is nothing," Kate said speaking very fast. "You need not be afraid. Nothing special happened before you had your accident. When you are better everything will go on just as it did before."

She watched his face closely, and it did not change: she saw that her lie had been detected and that Miles had got no comfort from it. There was nothing more to be said, and she left almost at once with a hurried kiss that she scarcely realised had been given.

"She would not have kissed me if there could still be anything between us," he said, and awaited his next dose of sedative with impatience.

Pounceforth's life at this time was far from happy. He foresaw that Honeychurch and the opinion of his colleagues would soon oblige him to give up his post; he foresaw that his pride would hardly stand in the way of an ignominious return to the library before his place there could be taken. He felt it would become him better to give his action at least the appearance of a personal benevolence by taking the step voluntarily, rather than waiting until it was forced upon him. This was not an easy thing to do. A series of events set in train by him, but hardly planned, had led to a result that planning could not have achieved. Latimer had been removed from the scene, and in circumstances that should have spelt disgrace; but the feeling Pounceforth had been at pains to create had recoiled upon its maker. It was seen that the hounding to death of Murivance was a figment of Pounceforth's imagination, whereas the hounding of Latimer was a process to which Prentice, Roberts and Hilary Scott had all borne witness. Nor had Pounceforth the comfort of knowing that the second act of self-destruction was as illusory as the first. He had, as Honeychurch had surmised, a conscience; it was not fastidious, but it existed; and during the four days when it seemed possible that Latimer might die, Pounceforth experienced a degree of suffering that Hilary would hardly have thought him capable of. With the news that the patient was showing some signs of recovery, he underwent a further revulsion of feeling. His thoughts turned upon himself and his future. He realised that the College might close its doors against him altogether, that he was no younger than Latimer and no more likely to find a job ready to hand. He needed a measure of security against his possible downfall, and there was only one place where this was to be found.

"Since you still draw a salary from the College, Scott, it might be advisable for you to spend a few moments here and there doing something to earn it. I do not know that the visitation of the sick is among the duties attached to your post."

Hilary said nothing.

"There are half a dozen articles here that I have read through, and none of the references has been checked. There is an annotation on coeliac disease that requires at least one illustration. These small matters should occupy you for the morning. During the afternoon you can work on the index for 1953: there are omissions under B and H; I have seen as much without having the time to correct them."

"Is that all you want done?"

"Well, there is more to do, but you won't have time for it. I have some business of my own to attend to this morning; I may even be away the rest of the day."

Hilary waited until he had gone and then went to the museum gallery. He found Prentice still busy with the catalogue.

"I am so glad to see you, Scott!"

"I shouldn't interrupt your work."

"Why do you think I am glad to see you? I see no particular virtue in work for its own sake."

"I would like to impress that point of view upon Pounceforth!"

"I wouldn't waste time in trying to alter Pounceforth if I were you. Of course, you are younger than I am, but still it would be time wasted. Did you want something?"

"Miles told Kate you had chosen some books and journals for his preliminary reading. She will take them to the nursing home if you can spare them, and somebody can read to him."

"It is just for interest's sake? He knows nothing will come of it?"

"How could we tell him that?"

"I see you couldn't. There are the things he needs, in that pile on my table. Take as many as you can manage. There are some more journals on the top shelf in Murivance's cupboard, I rather think. If you can get them down for me, I will pick out the ones he will find useful— I mean the ones he would like to read."

Hilary opened the door. The lower part of the cupboard was filled by the cabin trunk. He had seen it only on the day of the skeleton's arrival and had never thought to ask what had become of it. Now the red labels announcing its departure from St. Pancras struck him as incongruous. He removed the journals, waited for Prentice to make his selection, and then said with some diffidence, "Do you know where Pounceforth lives?"

"I do know, but it has slipped my mind. I will recall it in a moment. Why do you ask?"

"He has gone off for the day and left me with some work that I will not be able to finish without a word of assistance. I thought I might phone him."

"The beadle will have his number, I should think. Try there."

The beadle revealed that Pounceforth's number was on the Bayswater exchange. Hilary left the heap of journals with him together with a note for Kate and walked out of the College, turning north towards the Euston Road. He made his way to the Parcels Office at St. Pancras and stood in a short queue, wondering how best to put his questions.

"My name is Murivance. Four weeks ago I was sent a present; it was labelled as coming from this station, but the sender forgot to enclose his name and address. I have made enquiries, but he cannot be traced. I wonder if you keep a record of these things?"

"We do, sir, but it isn't available to everybody. If you will just step this way."

Hilary stepped this way, into a smaller, side room. A variety of people discussed his case before him, and at last something not unlike Mr. Trimble's order book appeared and was consulted.

"Could you give me a name at all, sir? There must be someone you have in mind."

"There is a man called Pounceforth."

"That is not the name we have here."

"He lives in Bayswater."

"And we have no address. The party brought the object, described as a cabin trunk, to this depot. It wasn't collected from a private address at all."

"You couldn't tell me the name?"

There were further discussions, and at last the man gave in.

"If it will do no harm, sir, if it will be of any help, the name was Smith."

"That is the other name I might have thought of," Hilary said.

"There is the gentleman again, the one with the funny name."

"I have come back," Hilary said, and was conscious of a superfluity. "I wondered if anybody would remember what Mr. Smith looked like."

"In two days' time, sir, I shall hardly remember what you look like, and you have an unusual name. It wouldn't be too much to say that I have seen hundreds of Smiths in my time. We all have."

"Smiths with cabin trunks they want to send to Murivances?"

"We are a very busy depot, sir."

"And I am wasting your time. Well, thank you. I have learnt something even if it was not quite what I hoped."

"You were asking about a Mr. Smith, sir, with a cabin trunk?"

Hilary saw that a porter had been following him.

"Yes. Do you know the man I mean?"

"I don't know that I do, sir, but I know a gentleman brought a trunk here a month ago. I carried it from his car. It was a queer thing to bring in a car; that's why I remember it."

"What did he look like? What sort of car was it?"

"He was a middle-aged chap, shorter than you and stouter built. Well dressed; he gave me a decent tip."

Hilary acted upon this suggestion.

"And the car. Do you remember anything about the car?"

"It was a Bentley, black, new. I didn't notice the number; there was no reason why I should. Are you a detective? Was there a body in the trunk?"

"I suppose, in a way, the answer to both those questions is yes. But it must go no further."

"I know when to keep my mouth shut."

"And I do not," Hilary said, but to himself.

Pounceforth, using a public telephone, dialled Sidney Berringer's number and was told by the receptionist that Mr. Berringer was engaged; would he call back later? Pounceforth would not; he explained that his business was urgent and begged that his name be taken to the surgeon immediately. As he had expected, Berringer shortly greeted him. Telephones tend to the blurring of subtle distinctions of tone, but Pounceforth believed he could trace both fear and eagerness in this voice; the fear he found encouraging, the eagerness warned him to play his cards cautiously.

"There is something I can do for you, Dr. Pounceforth?"

"The reverse situation was in my mind," Pounceforth said discreetly. "However, there is no need to quibble. I should be glad of the chance to talk to you."

"I will give you my home address."

"I would prefer not to visit you there. I thought we might have a little ride together."

"My car is at your disposal."

"In a public vehicle. You may not find it as convenient as your car, but it will be more comfortable for me."

"A public vehicle!"

"A number twenty-four bus, to be precise. I will meet you at the Warren Street stop at eleven-thirty if the time suits you."

After a prolonged and perhaps meaningful pause, Berringer's voice agreed to the meeting place and the time. Pounceforth rang off and was annoyed but hardly surprised to see that his hand was wet with perspiration.

"You are playing with fire, Dr. Pounceforth," Berringer remarked when they met an hour later. There was a queue at the bus stop and he spoke in an irritable whisper. Part of his irritation was social; it upset him to be rubbing shoulders with clerks, shop girls and students; he felt and looked out of place. Nobody else in the queue wore a bowler with a black morning coat and pinstriped trousers; nobody else had a pink carnation in his buttonhole. This he had intended to remove before he left his consulting rooms, but it had seemed at the last moment too much like hauling down his flag. "Murder," he said, "is a more presentable crime than blackmail. I owe it to myself to assert the greater dignity of my position." Consequently he had retained his carnation, and was now suffering the faintly hostile stare of other persons waiting to catch the number twenty-four bus.

"Where will this bus take us when it comes?" he demanded, allowing his glance to dwell one moment upon his companion before he withdrew it in confusion. Pounceforth's dress was no more suited to the occasion than his own, but whereas his own in other circumstances had seemed appropriate and even elegant, no circumstances could have justified Pounceforth's cap of shepherd's plaid or his scarf, boldly striped in navy blue and yellow, worn with a fawn hacking jacket, corduroy trousers and golfing socks.

"To Hampstead Heath," Pounceforth said, meeting Berringer's disapproval with a fine disregard. "And back again, and again and again, if necessary, until we conclude our business."

"We shall make ourselves conspicuous," Berringer protested.

"We cannot be more conspicuous than we are. Everyone is looking at us; it is almost as if we were royalty," Pounceforth said smiling amicably to left and right. "We are being labelled as a pair of eccentrics: as a pair, if you follow me. It is a point of some importance, to me at least."

They climbed onto a bus, ascended to the upper deck on Pounceforth's directions, and sat side by side halfway along the aisle. Other people occupied the front seats and those at the very back, but the two men were substantially isolated. Pounceforth knew the habits of bus travellers from many years' experience; he took a malicious delight in Berringer's plain discomfiture.

"Here, as you see, we can talk without fear of being overheard or interrupted." The conductor approached them. "If you will take tickets, Berringer: two to the Heath is what you ask for."

Berringer bought two tickets, handed one to Pounceforth, and sat staring ahead in a brooding silence; his own ticket he retained, holding it firmly in one chamois-gloved hand as if it were a talisman. The bus moved off. Pounceforth settled back easily and remarked on the weather.

"I see no point in pretending that we are here to discuss the weather," Berringer said coldly. "Either this is a commercial transaction or it is nothing at all. My time is valuable, if yours is not."

Pounceforth assumed a look of sympathy. "I know this tension must be unbearable for you. You are wondering how much I know."

"I am wondering how much you want."

"It comes to the same thing," Pounceforth said indifferently. "I know a great deal and it goes against the grain to keep it to myself. Gossip is the staff of life to me, and a subject as exciting as this has never come my way before. So you will have to pay me twice as much for my silence as you would have to pay a naturally uncommunicative person. I shall have to keep a continual curb on my tongue and that will impose a strain."

"I shall pay you nothing. I am not a fool. I know that the first demand will not be the last."

"Of course it will not," Pounceforth agreed. "Neither of us is a fool. For years, Berringer, I have longed to make money on the stock exchange, but I have never had the capital. Your misdemeanour shall be my capital, and I see no reason why it should not pay a regular dividend. Five hundred pounds half-yearly was what I had in mind, tax-free. The exact amount will rest with me: the market may fluctuate but the value of my holding in it is likely to remain constant. Unless of course the death penalty is abolished. And even then a man of your tastes and habits would prefer to avoid life imprisonment, if I am not mistaken."

"You are mad," Berringer said vehemently. "What can you prove? Nothing! If I say that I have no idea what you are talking about, what can you do?"

"This is Camden Town," Pounceforth said. "We are almost halfway to Hampstead, and if you had no idea what I was talking about you would not be here. There is no need for me to find proof. If I go to the police and tell them what I have seen, they will find the proof for me. That is their business. They will know that that girl is missing; they cannot dig all over England to find her. I can show them where to dig."

"She had no friends. No one could link her name with mine."

"The police would find a link. She came from somewhere, somebody will have missed her. You cannot be sure you were never seen together."

A silence told Pounceforth that Berringer could not be sure.

"And I saw you take her into the wood and come out again alone. I saw you pick up the spade I had dropped: I watched you and put two and two together. You brought the spade back when you had finished with it, and wiped the handle clean. It never occurred to you to wonder why it was there. Later you saw the news of our discoveries in the newspapers, our brilliant discoveries, the triumph of the amateur archaeologist. I know you saw the news, because I went to the trouble of sending you cuttings. Finally I sent you a skeleton: I have sometimes wondered if that was an unnecessary extravagance on my part. It was intended to soften you up. Did it soften you up, do you think?"

"You have made yourself an accessory after the fact," Berringer said.

"But my guilt could hardly be established if yours were not established first. I believe my price would be easier to pay, wouldn't it? Here we are, at our destination. Wait here one moment."

The top of the bus emptied. Pounceforth ran down the stairs.

"My friend and I wish to stay and make the return journey with you. You don't mind?"

"I don't mind," the conductor said, accepting eccentricity with as much or as little attention as he would have given a foreign coin; and went off for a cup of tea with a story to tell.

"I could deal with you here and now," Berringer remarked as Pounceforth sat down again beside him. "We are out of sight. I could put my hands round your neck, and then walk off this bus and catch another; that trolleybus over there, for instance."

"You will do nothing of the sort," Pounceforth said calmly. "Why do you think I chose to wear this preposterous costume? Dozens of people have seen us together, and they have not just seen us. They have looked and looked again. If my body were found in this bus, every one of them could give an accurate description of you. And I have seen to it that the conductor knows you and I are alone up here."

Berringer sat in silence, turning over a succession of plans in his head. "You will give me time to think this over?" he said at last.

"Not much time. Today is Monday. Next weekend, next Saturday, four of us are going down to Throckleford to cover the mosaic over before the winter sets in. Frost might break it up, so it has to be protected."

"I know that," Berringer said crisply. "It would surprise you to learn how many books on this subject I have read recently."

"What did you learn from them? What did you hope to learn? Whether our villa might extend under the wood, if it were part of a whole settlement, for instance? Well, it is something, to have widened your field of knowledge! We shall be going down there with all the equipment we need. I shall take a few denarii of the right period with me; I shall wander into the trees, reasonably enough. I shall discover some loose earth and a coin or two. Have some children of the district followed up our finds and extended the dig to the woods?—I shall ask. So of course we shall dig a little further, and you know what will be under the ground. I think you had better come to a decision before Saturday. On Friday at the latest I shall expect to hear from you."

"You shall hear from me. I promise you that."

Passengers filled the seats around them. Pounceforth made pleasant conversation for these anonymous protectors' ears all the way back to the Euston Road; he should perhaps have seen cause for alarm in the ease with which Berringer joined in this esoteric game. But he did not: he was not so intelligent as he believed.

Honeychurch put his head round the door of Pounceforth's office just after luncheon on the same day. Pounceforth had not yet come back; Hilary was sitting at his desk doing the *Times* crossword. It was to his credit in the circumstances that he made no effort to pretend that he was working. The effort would in any case have been wasted, for Honeychurch was preoccupied.

"Would you be going to see Latimer this afternoon, Dr. Scott?"

"I will if you want me to," Hilary said with alacrity. "Is it to take a message?"

"Not to Miles himself. Mr. Murivance's solicitor has just spoken to me on the telephone. His sister is in London to wind up his affairs: one of the things she plans to do is to make a visit to his flat, and Miles had the only key last Tuesday when he went there. If you could spare the time to meet her at the flat, collecting the key on the way——"

"I'll leave at once. What time will she be there? What is her name?"

"She is a Mrs. Hale. And she will be at the flat at half past three."

Hilary left the College with a light heart, drove to the nursing home and went straight to the sister's room.

"Has Dr. Latimer remembered his visit to Mr. Murivance's flat yet? Can I ask him about it, Sister? I want the key to give to the solicitors and I thought I should ask your permission before I broached the subject to him."

"Nobody has tried to prod his memory," she said. "That

would be going directly against Mr. Berringer's instructions. So you see we have no way of being sure whether he remembers a thing or not. He has said nothing about the day of the accident yet to any of us, and it would be better not to say anything ourselves. Would you like to go through the things he was wearing when he came in? All his possessions are in the cupboard in his room. I will come with you: I believe he is asleep."

"Asleep!" Hilary repeated. "At this time of day?"

"He still has bad nights and frightening dreams. He sleeps a good deal in the daytime; and he is being helped to sleep, on Mr. Berringer's directions."

Hilary went through the pockets of Miles's suit and coat with a feeling of intrusion. There were all the things that usually fill a man's pockets, including a key ring. This he took away with him, after Sister had made an entry in the appropriate book and signatures had been formally appended. At half past three he met Mrs. Hale on the stairs outside Mr. Murivance's flat, and found her a shorter, plumper, younger version of her brother, with eyes that hardship seemed to have narrowed in a glance of steady mistrust.

"Have I kept you waiting? I do apologise. Now, I don't know which of these keys is the one we want. It is odd that Miles should have put it on his own ring."

"It is not so very odd," she said coldly. "He probably felt himself to have a right to all my brother's possessions."

Hilary kept silent, but with an effort. He tried first one key and then another in the Yale lock. Neither fitted; none of the others were of the right kind.

Mrs. Hale did not bother to conceal her annoyance. "Let me try, please!"

He took a certain unkind pleasure in watching her try a number of quite unsuitable keys.

Finally she handed them back to him. "It has obviously been lost. I should have thought your friend might at least have taken the trouble to safeguard another person's property."

"It is only because he took so little trouble to safeguard his own that you are here now, Mrs. Hale. I will go back to the nursing home and see what I can do. Shall I pass the key on to the solicitors when I find it? It seems ridiculous to waste any more of your time."

She consented with an ill grace; they left the building under a cloud of strong mutual hostility, and Hilary allowed her to catch a bus before he got into his own car, a gesture so much at variance with his own better feelings that he drove off in a thoroughly bad temper. Wimpole Street was nearer than St. John's Wood, and on an impulse he drove to Berringer's consulting rooms first. Berringer would be pleased to see him, the receptionist said when she had taken in his name, but the look on Berringer's face when Hilary went into his room was not one of unmixed pleasure. It was the first time Hilary had met the man, and he did not know how pale a shadow of his ordinary self Berringer was this afternoon; he did notice a slight tremor in the hand that shook his own, but put it down to the wrong emotion. His errand was quickly explained.

"That key!" Berringer said immediately. "How foolish of me to have forgotten it! I picked it up off the floor when the men were carrying Dr. Latimer up to the ambulance. Let me give it to you at once—or would you rather that I took it to the solicitors myself? It would be unforgivable of me to give you extra trouble when I have caused so much already."

"It is no trouble at all," Hilary said truthfully. "The solicitors are in Lincoln's Inn Fields, not five minutes away from Caroline Square. I will finish the job now I have started it."

"Where did I put the key? I wonder." Berringer murmured, running a hand through his abundant, silvering hair. "In this drawer, I expect. Yes, here it is."

Hilary thanked him, they exchanged farewells that seemed to both of them too prolonged to suit so simple an occasion, and he left Berringer tapping a nervous forefinger on his bureau. When he was in his car, an idea came to him. He sat thoughtfully at the wheel, staring ahead, wondering if there could be the faintest justification for what he meant to do. Finally he put his scruples aside, drove back to Mr. Murivance's flat, and was soon inside it. There were half a dozen envelopes lying by the door; he picked them up and added them to a pile already on the table. Then he began to look round, not knowing what he was looking for. There was thick dust on every surface, dead flowers on the mantelshelf, dead coals and ashes in the grate. On the top of the bureau was a large book. He looked at it without picking it up; *Art Treasures of the Western World*, the gilt letters on its spine announced. It hardly sounded the sort of book to appeal to Mr. Murivance, but that gentleman's tastes might have been more eclectic than Hilary had guessed. His fingers strayed towards it, but the dust repelled him; he looked at it again quickly, and then at the top of the bureau itself. His pulse quickened, he ran across to the table, picked up the pile of letters and sifted through them rapidly. This cannot be true, he told himself, but seeing his own face in a mirror, with a look of unholy excitement on it, "It must be true," he said.

Professor Honeychurch was leading a discussion at the Royal Society of Medicine. Hilary drove to Wigmore Street and parked his car in a side turning. A fine drizzle had begun to fall, and hours seemed to him to elapse before the familiar figure lumbered down the steps surrounded by the usual cluster of eager questioners, detractors, adulators. Hilary pushed his way through them; the look on his face had not changed, and Honeychurch saw the matter was urgent, as the subject of the late discussion had not been. He made his apologies and was soon on the way back to Caroline Square, sitting in silent astonishment while Hilary recounted his adventures of the afternoon.

"It seemed so odd," Hilary said, "that just that key and nothing else should have fallen out of Miles's pockets; I didn't see quite how odd at the time. But then I realised that somebody else must have been in the flat since Miles left it."

"Can you be sure of that, Dr. Scott?"

"I can be positive. I picked up two advertising circulars off the floor as I went in. There were about a dozen other letters on a little side table. Six of them were dated before the twentieth, when Miles went there. But there were two actually stamped on the twentieth, and they were both posted for late collections. Another visitor must have picked them up automatically, as I did. Even if Miles put some of them on the table, he could not have handled the last two."

"But now all the letters are together," Honeychurch

said thoughtfully, "and nobody witnessed your actions. It will never be possible to prove what you have just told me, to anyone else's satisfaction."

"But to us it proves that Sidney Berringer is deeper in this business than we thought. He must have been the second visitor."

"There might be other keys," Honeychurch objected.

"The solicitors would probably have known if there were, and Mrs. Hale could have had access to the flat without their bothering us. And anyway, that complicates the issue still more, instead of simplifying it."

Hilary drew up outside the College and they sat in the car, unwilling to traverse the few yards of wet pavement and wetter atmosphere between themselves and the main entrance. Both stared ahead as if profound embarrassment absolved them from looking at each other.

"There is really no reason," Honeychurch said at last, "why Berringer should not visit his old patient's flat."

"And there is no reason we know of why he should."

"Those statements might with equal truth be applied nearer home, Dr. Scott. Why did *you* go there?"

"On impulse. Berringer might have done the same. But that would not have accounted for the book."

"You are keeping something up your sleeve!" Honeychurch said indignantly. "There is something you haven't told me. Well, what is it?"

"A large book on the bureau had a thin layer of dust on it. There was thicker dust on the bureau itself. It is the story of the adrenaline bottle and syringe all over again, but this time we cannot blame Pounceforth for it. It was not the sort of book Mr. Murivance would have had; that was another thing I noticed."

"You think Berringer left it there? But that would have been extraordinarily careless of him!"

"I doubt if it were careless," Hilary said with a frown. "I think it suggests a good deal of caution. Supposing it replaced another large book that Miles had taken away?"

"You must explain this to me; I am at a loss."

"Sister at the nursing home told me that Miles had given Berringer back a little volume of poems that Mr. Murivance had borrowed. But if it were a large book, not a little one? And if there had been a clean space on the bureau where the book had lain?"

"But why should Berringer have lied about this? Oh, I see why: because the book that Miles did in fact return to him had some significance. We are getting into very deep water, Dr. Scott. I am not sure that I like so much conjecture and so few facts. And we have nothing against Berringer. What could have prompted him to such curious behaviour?"

"Have we nothing against him? Mr. Murivance left his consulting rooms and died a few hours later; Miles barely got off the premises with his life. Can that be just a coincidence?"

Honeychurch said finally, "We are most likely making mountains out of molehills. We know there is no mystery about Mr. Murivance. He must have died a natural death. When Miles remembers what has happened to him, he will probably be able to dispel any doubts we may have had about his fall; and he will satisfy us over this matter of the book, too."

"That is a thought that might also have occurred to Berringer."

"You have made some shrewd guesses, Dr. Scott, but

they have not convinced me, and I don't believe they would convince anyone else. Do you mean to follow them up?"

"With your permission."

"I don't know what you mean, with my permission," Honeychurch said testily. "I am well aware that what I say or think will make no difference whatever. Well, I confess, Dr. Scott, I share your love of the oddities and quirks of human behaviour; but I am less ready than you are to make a man out a double murderer simply as a diversion. For that is what you imply, if I am not mistaken—that Berringer pushed Miles over his balustrade?"

"That is what happened; I am sure of it."

"It behoves me to reserve judgement. If you can show me that there are any real grounds for connecting Berringer with the rest of this affair, I will change my mind. I trust you not to behave foolishly and hotheadedly. I hope I can trust you."

"You can trust me," Hilary said, "and I think I can convince you here and now. Look."

A car had turned into Caroline Square from the Southampton Row end. It came to a stop facing them; Kate Cardew jumped out and stood at the kerbside for a moment, thanking the driver. And the driver was Berringer, and the car was a great black Bentley.

"And the hair, the beautiful thick hair," Hilary said, "is only a transformation, in the truest sense of the word."

VII

Kate had spent her afternoon preparing Professor Honeychurch's notes for the discussion and getting the morning's
letters ready for his signature. When he left the College
she had nothing more to do. Hilary was not yet back from
his errand; she collected the sheaf of journals from the beadle and went off to St. John's Wood. By the time she
reached the nursing home, it was already dark and damp;
it was with a sense of relief that she pushed open the heavy
doors and stepped into the entrance hall. The warmth inside seemed stifling; the light grated on her eyes; other visitors to other patients moved up and down the wide staircase, most of them women, many of them perfectly
dressed. Kate was conscious of looking well herself; she had
walked quickly from the bus stop; her stockings might be
splashed, but her cheeks were in a glow and her short, un-
covered hair was misted with the fine rain. She was excited,
although she hardly knew why. She was on her way to read
three dismal papers on the pathogenesis of congenital pul-
monary disease to a man whose muffled overtures she had
tacitly rejected only a few weeks before. The mission was
dull enough on the surface, but under the surface was an
agitation she did not want to examine too closely or just
yet. Kate was sufficiently near to being in love to prefer not
to think about it, and she would rather have taken herself
unawares than stopped on her way to Miles to wonder at

her longing to be with him again. But, looking about her as she came to the top of the stairs, uncertain for a moment which door was his, she suddenly saw that this was an expensive place, that a room here must cost many guineas a week. Miles had few guineas, and would be here for months. "Who is to pay for it?" she said to herself, and "Why didn't Berringer send him to a hospital? In most places they would have found a private room for him. Presumably he felt he was to blame for the accident and this is his way of making amends." But she remembered that Miles was touchy about money and likely to be more embarrassed than pleased by this form of reparation.

The sister came out of one of the rooms, closing the door behind her with great caution.

"No, he is awake," she said in answer to Kate's unspoken question, "but I am in a dilemma, Miss Cardew. He isn't as well as he was on Saturday; he seems restless and excited again. I am not at all sure that he should have a visitor today."

Kate bit her lip as she had done long years before when a promised picnic had been postponed because of the weather, the bicycle she had longed for forbidden because her father thought it was too dangerous. Her eagerness was replaced by an obstinacy just as unreasonable. "I shall not disturb him," she said lightly but stubbornly. "I have only brought some books he wanted; they are not at all exciting. If I just sit down and read quietly it might do some good, don't you think? Mightn't it calm him to be read to for a little while?"

No picnic, no bicycle, Sister's look announced, but she said rather unwillingly, "Go in for a few minutes, then. But you must leave when I come to tell you."

The room was dismal by artificial light, Kate thought,

too tall for its floor space, the one window high and the curtains not yet drawn. She drew them after a hurried greeting, turning away to hide her access of anxiety.

"It is good of you to come, Kate. Is it raining?"

"Not much. Enough for me to be glad to be out of it. This room is warm, isn't it? Wouldn't you like the window open? The curtains will keep out the draught."

"Just as you wish," he said with weary indifference, and watched her as she arranged the curtains again, moved a chair nearer to his bedside, laid her coat over another chair; making the bare room come alive and the gloom recede.

"What do you want me to read to you?" she said. "I have brought the articles you asked for. Prentice said the one in the *Archives of Diseases of Childhood* for the last quarter would be the most useful. Shall I start on that?"

"Thank you, Kate."

"You must tell me if I go too fast."

She cleared her throat and began to read in a low, even, subdued voice. She understood most of what she was reading and was prepared to share his interest, was keyed up to notice the slightest response, but none came. When she reached the end of the first section, she looked up.

"Go on reading, Kate."

"But you are not listening!"

"Not to the words. It is pointless for me to listen to the words. But I like to hear your voice."

She read a few more sentences, then put the journal down with a little snort of exasperation. "What do you mean, Miles, about its being pointless for you to listen to the words?"

"I have remembered what everyone has been at such pains to keep me from remembering. So you need not pretend any more. It's a good thing you need not, because deception is so difficult for you, Kate."

"How much do you remember?" she said slowly.

"Enough for the present. Going to the solicitor's office and not having any money, or a job. I know I went back to the College to clear up my things; I talked to Prentice, didn't I? After that, there's still a blank. Why are you smiling suddenly, Kate? Is there something else you were afraid I might know about? Why does there have to be all this secrecy?"

"It is for your own sake, Dr. Latimer," Berringer said soothingly.

Kate sprang to her feet. "How quietly you came in, Mr. Berringer!"

"I knocked," Berringer said, accepting the need to lie philosophically enough, "but you must have been too absorbed to hear me. I am sorry to have interrupted your tête-à-tête. I thought my patient would be alone and sleeping. I would prefer him to be asleep."

"Kate's presence is not upsetting me, if that is what you mean," Miles said. "I may be upsetting myself, I daresay. I cannot see why I am not to be told what has happened to me. I don't believe I can have done anything so very terrible! Unless I had one of those fashionable blackouts and killed somebody without knowing what I was doing."

"Of course you didn't!" Kate said quickly.

"You tried to," Berringer said with some amusement. "As to the blackout or not, we can none of us say. And it was only yourself you were doing away with, so the matter rests between us."

"Mr. Berringer!"

"Don't look so startled, Miss Cardew. Dr. Latimer would certainly have remembered his action in a few days, and I have merely saved him the trouble of probing about for the memory. Fretting, fidgeting, mentally fretting and fidgeting, I mean, are things he must avoid."

"I tried to kill myself?" Miles said.

"Yes, and on my premises. Don't think I am taxing you with being inconsiderate! If you had chosen another time or place or method I should never have made Miss Cardew's acquaintance, and that is compensation enough."

Kate accepted this formal gallantry for what it was worth; her eyes were on Miles, and his eyes were closed. Neither observed that Berringer was a good deal more excited than his patient.

"I suppose he may be right," Miles said as if to himself. "There were good enough reasons."

"There are not so many now," Kate said with urgency and put her hand over his.

"It was outside your rooms," Miles said, turning to Berringer with sudden conviction, "there was a balustrade and I walked over to look at it."

"Not just to look at it," Berringer said archly. "That was what I thought you were doing, but there was something else in your mind."

"I jumped over it? That sounds much too energetic for me. I am the sort of person who would take an overdose of barbiturate and go quietly to sleep."

"But my balustrade came more readily to hand than your barbiturate. And you acted on impulse. None of us knows how we would act at such a crisis until we have already acted."

"I surprise myself more and more," Miles said, and saw from Kate's expression that his lightness had both astounded and pleased her. "Will you leave us together for a moment, Berringer?"

"I don't think you should talk any more just now," Berringer said swiftly. "You must bear in mind that I don't want you to excite yourself. I have told you the whole story to keep you from uneasy speculation, and you must demonstrate your gratitude by doing as I tell you. You are not to keep turning these things over and over; it will do you no good. It would be better for you not to recapture too exactly the feelings that led you to do it."

"I want to recapture other feelings," Miles said, "ones that would tend another way."

"Not now," Berringer said. "You need be in no hurry, Latimer. Miss Cardew will come and see you again. I believe I can promise him that, Miss Cardew?"

"Of course I will come again. If you really think I should go, Mr. Berringer——" Kate said.

"I really do, I really do."

"Then, goodbye, Miles. The picnic has been postponed again."

"What do you mean?"

"I will tell you next time I come."

Berringer said firmly, "I can give you a lift, Miss Cardew, if you will tell me which way you are going. And now, will you permit me the favour I refuse you? I want a moment with my patient."

Kate picked up her coat, kissed Miles with resolution, and left the room.

Berringer said easily, "I repeat, you are not to brood on things, Latimer. Remember that for a short time you must have been what is popularly called 'of unsound mind.' Your impressions of that time are likely to be distorted, and to recall them too vividly might induce a return to the same state. You follow me?"

It was clear to him from the sudden look of fear on

Miles's face that his point had been taken. He smiled encouragingly, patted the plaster-covered wrist lying on the sheet, and withdrew. A moment later, Sister came into the room with a syringe on a dish.

"What is that?"

"Mr. Berringer wants you to have a good night's sleep."

"I could sleep soundly tonight without anything. I don't want to be kept drugged."

"Hush! You have no choice in the matter. You have shown that you cannot be trusted to act in your own best interests."

Miles submitted to the injection. The sister was surprised at his resentment and made a note of it in her report. Night Sister, a loquacious and cheerful woman, read this out to her nurses when she came on duty some hours later, and added her own comment: 'As I have said before and will say again, you never can tell with head injuries. First they're up, then they're down. One day they're as quiet as mice, the next they're climbing up the curtains. None of you girls need be surprised if Dr. Latimer comes out with some queer things just now. Come and tell me if you're worried, that's all. A little more of *this*," she tapped the hyoscine ampoule with an authoritative finger, "will keep him happy. Mr. Berringer has written it all down."

Honeychurch took Hilary and Kate up to his room. They made up the fire and pulled their chairs close to it. After ten minutes, each was in possession of the other's experiences. Honeychurch, who had nothing of his own to contribute, listened to what they had to say with increasing gravity.

"Let us see what we have so far," he said at length. "Pounceforth's skeleton was Murivance's skeleton, sent to him by Sidney Berringer, who was concerned to hide his own identity. Later Mr. Murivance died, we don't know how or why. Miles took Berringer a book he found in Murivance's flat and fell or was pushed and is lucky to be alive. Berringer possibly visited Murivance's flat himself to disguise the nature of the book Miles brought him, and also lied at least about its size, and perhaps its nature, though that we cannot say. And now he has told Miles about his fall; perhaps he has intervened before any memory of the book could come back. What can we make of all this?"

"Two things," Hilary said at once. "Pounceforth is not as important as we thought; he seemed to be a prime mover, but he had no hand whatever in the two intended deaths. And the other thing is the book. It must have been important: Miles had never seen Berringer before and yet he had to be killed when he introduced himself with the book. If only we could find it! I suppose I couldn't break into Berringer's consulting rooms?"

"He is an efficient person," Honeychurch said with promptitude, "and the book would certainly not be there. He may even have destroyed it."

"Miles will know what it was," Kate said, on an indrawn breath. "Can't we get him out of that place? Berringer will try to prevent him telling us, and he is so absolutely helpless."

"He is pent in durance vile," Hilary said, "and all so publicly. Berringer has played his cards very well."

"My dear, you must not be so alarmed," Honeychurch said to Kate. "We cannot believe that everyone in that nursing home is corrupt; it is not likely that Berringer could attack a patient and get away with it."

"But it does not matter whether he could get away with

it or not," Kate said miserably. "It is the attack that matters—that would matter, I mean, if he chose to make it.
Surely Miles could be moved, transferred to a hospital;
surely there must be a way!"

Honeychurch said ruefully, "It would be very difficult,
next to impossible, I greatly fear. If there were a close relation who wanted him moved it might be different."

"But if we were to insist?"

"How could we insist? Berringer would say, quite correctly, that to move him at all so soon after such injuries
would be to take an appalling risk. And who are we to insist
to? To Berringer himself! No reasons we could give would
weigh an ounce against his intentions."

"We might go to the police!" she said, and in despair,
"but of course there is nothing to tell the police. And even
then we might be too late. I will go back there and stay
with him. He is safe for a few hours at least. Berringer told
me he was going to a dinner at the British Orthopaedic Association. Can't we take it in turns to stay with Miles?"

She looked from one to the other. Honeychurch's face
was doubtful, Hilary's showed a gleam of excitement.

"I will help, Kate. I believe the sister would be on our
side if we told her everything. She doesn't like Berringer;
she almost said as much."

"Not liking Berringer is far from being the same thing as
believing our story," Honeychurch said. "No reasonable
creature would believe it, not as it stands. But somebody
must be with Miles, that is clear."

"This is a nightmare," Kate said, and shuddered. "I was
there with both of them and I left them alone together.
Nothing could have happened already, could it?"

Nobody said anything. Honeychurch was thinking of
Mr. Murivance, who died some hours after leaving Ber-

ringer and with no marks of violence. Hilary was thinking of Kate and trying to accustom himself to thinking of Kate and Miles together if Miles survived.

"I have it!" Honeychurch said at last and in triumph. "I wonder if my telephone will function at this late hour?"

"I will go down and connect up the switchboard for you," Kate said, jumping up, alight at the prospect of doing something useful.

"There is no need," Honeychurch said with the receiver to his ear. "The instrument is making the correct noises. Now, if I remember rightly the number is Goodwin seven eight seven eight." He paused a moment. "I remembered rightly. Charles, after all these years I remembered your number!" He put a hand over the mouthpiece and told Hilary, "This is Charles Abbott, the psychiatrist. A good friend of mine at one time." Into the telephone he said, "Of course it's Fabian, and of course I want something of you: it takes necessity to revive a lapsed friendship. I would like your advice about an acquaintance of mine who recently attempted to commit suicide. Yes, it is urgent. There is always a chance he might try again."

VIII

During the course of the next three hours, Honeychurch
sat fuming by his telephone, sporadically talking to various
persons at County Hall who assured him that the Duly
Authorised Officer was engaged elsewhere, was still engaged elsewhere, had not yet returned from his engagement, could not be found, would no doubt soon be available, was very busy tonight; this last was evident from the
rest, and Honeychurch mused sadly on the glimpse given
by these diverse hints into the numbers of insane or poten-
tially insane people within the County of London, for the
Duly Authorised Officer was the man to get in touch with,
Charles Abbott had said, if you wanted to report curious,
perhaps certifiable behaviour on the part of a friend or
relation. Without a single qualm, Honeychurch placed
Miles in this category and set out to protect him from Sidney Berringer by the simpler expedient of protecting him
from himself. Hilary drove Kate back to his rooms and
they returned laden with sandwiches and a thermos of
coffee. Kate found cups and saucers in Prentice's cupboard
and they enjoyed, or failed to enjoy, an alfresco meal in
the intervals between telephone calls. Eventually the Duly
Authorised Officer spoke himself. He had, Honeychurch
reported, a friendly and accommodating voice. He promised to meet them outside the nursing home at half past

ten, and came to the tryst in an ambulance, wearing a thick check muffler and an air of tired affability.

"It is the next step that will be difficult," Honeychurch said in an undertone to Hilary. "I don't see what we can do if the night sister refuses to let us in."

"Refuses to let me in!" said the Duly Authorised Officer, catching the last words. "Nobody ever refuses to let me in. They'd better not. Once the case has been reported to me I have to see it, even if it means getting a police warrant to look over the premises. Don't you worry about that, Professor. If you think your friend isn't being looked after the way he should be considering his state of mind, that's good enough for me."

The night sister turned out to be quite as aware of the officer's powers as anyone could have wished. She showed surprise at his visit but no displeasure, seeming, rather, to welcome a departure from routine; and accepted the arrival of three others at this late hour as a reasonable tribute to her patient's hidden determination to bypass the more conventional ways of leaving her charge. There was indeed one moment, while they stood uneasily by the sleeping Miles, when she remarked disquietingly that she would have thought it a better plan to inform the officer before this.

"It isn't nice for the young girls on my staff to have to deal with such a case. Supposing one of them were to come in and find the patient doing himself some harm?"

"He was stunned at first," Honeychurch said hastily. "As long as he was unconscious there was no need to be worried about him. But now we have reason to believe his depression may be returning."

The Duly Authorised Officer seemed perplexed.

"He can't do much to himself, surely, not in that state?"

It seemed to Honeychurch that the officer's gaze rested squarely upon the plastered wrist. He said, plausibly enough, "He is left-handed."

"He could smash a feeding cup and cut his throat with the fragments," said the sister unexpectedly, "or tear his sheet up and hang himself from the top of the bed. Or get down under the blankets and smother himself." She was silent, meeting four pairs of astonished eyes. "You never know what these people will get up to if their hearts are really set on it," she concluded in a businesslike way, "and it says in my report that he has been restless and difficult today."

"Well, you won't be wanting me to have him moved to a mental observation ward, I take it?" the Duly Authorised Officer remarked. "I mean, it would be a bit of a nuisance getting all this business into an ambulance. Better have a policeman come in and sit by him, if you are worried. That would clear everybody's conscience, wouldn't it?"

"Mr. Berringer might object to a policeman," Night Sister said with disapproval. "Some of his patients are very influential and it wouldn't do for their visitors to see policemen going in and out. Would it be a uniformed policeman?"

"Most likely," said the Duly Authorised Officer.

"The visitors will probably assume that the patient in here is even more influential than the rest if he has a policeman at his beck and call. They will think a senior politician at the very least, perhaps even a member of the Cabinet, occupies the room." Honeychurch stopped, dazed with his own flight of fancy. "Yes, that is certainly what I would think in the circumstances."

"Of course, Mr. Berringer knows all about this?" Night Sister said, and frowned slightly.

"Of course he does," Hilary, Honeychurch, and Kate said with one voice.

"He told me only this evening——" Kate said.

"He has warned us that the need might arise," Honeychurch said.

"He will be delighted to find that we have anticipated his wishes," Hilary said.

"I will get on to the police for you," said the Duly Authorised Officer.

Berringer was not delighted.

"Why, what is this, Sister? What is this man doing here?"

"This is the one on duty at present, sir. The other one went away shortly after breakfast."

"Then, what was the other one doing here? Why did he come? Who sent him?"

"I believe it was the Duly Authorised Officer, Mr. Berringer. It was thought that Dr. Latimer's increased restlessness made some supervision necessary."

"It was thought! Who thought it?"

"The Duly Authorised Officer."

Berringer stood stock-still in the doorway, regarding the policeman with a look in which incredulity and rage were nicely blended. Miles also looked at the policeman, seeing him as it were through a haze compounded of the aftereffects of hyoscine and a disbelief that complemented but did not echo Berringer's. The policeman considered his own hands, and Sister watched Berringer.

"When did the Duly Authorised Officer come? Who sent for him?"

"Some friends of Dr. Latimer's gave the information

and came with him. Night Sister understood that it was done with your permission."

"What friends were these?" Berringer asked in a tone of controlled curiosity.

"I never thought to enquire. I assumed that you had arranged it all yourself. After Miss Cardew's visit last night, you told me you suspected a serious deterioration in the patient's condition."

"Of course I arranged it myself," Berringer said with marked irritation. "Such a thing could only have been done with my authority. I felt it best in the circumstances that a closer watch should be kept on him. It was hardly fair on you, Sister, or on your nurses."

He met her look of overwhelming scepticism with a bland smile of reassurance, and was not the first to turn away. When she finally made a move towards the bed, he also moved, shaking his head at Miles in gentle disapprobation and expanding his smile momentarily to include the policeman in a knowledgeable complicity.

"Well, Latimer, how are you this morning? It is a beautiful day for November, is it not? Blustery, but not too cold."

He was, it seemed to Miles, twice normal size and blurred about the edges; the reasoned jolliness of his manner was terrible. With a great effort, Miles produced a greeting, a remark about the sunshine.

Berringer exploded into laughter. "Try to sound a little more convinced, dear fellow! There is everything to live for on such a day as this. Why, Christmas is coming!"

The policeman laughed too. Miles met the sister's eye, and he struggled to retain the impression of her genuine concern.

"It is often said," Berringer told the room at large, "that depression only gets worse when the weather gets better. I wonder if there could be any truth in that? Certainly our friend here seems a little low in spirits today."

"You talk as if I were not here," Miles said with indignation, "or as if I cannot hear you or understand you. I am in full possession of my faculties."

Berringer smiled sympathetically. "Of course you are! You are talking like a rational being. It is only your mood that seems at variance with what we might expect. We shall have no cause for alarm until you begin to see or imagine things, isn't that so, Officer?"

The policeman was not sure what answer was expected of him, but judged it wiser to acquiesce.

"And how is the memory this morning, Latimer?" Berringer asked with the courage born of a desperate necessity to know where he stood. "Have you remembered any more of the events of last Tuesday?"

Miles said heavily, "I have slept ever since you left me last night. You give me no chance to remember."

"Good for you! It is better not to brood, that's what I told you, and you seem to be carrying out my orders. Now, off you go to sleep again. You are in good hands here, you know."

He signalled Sister to leave the room with him and in her office suggested a further dose of hyoscine. "I will come in to see him again this afternoon. I will not hide my anxiety from you. I am sure he has changed for the worse even since yesterday."

"He is still muddled and incoherent from his last injection. It would be something to wonder at if he were cheerful and lucid after so much sedation!"

"There is more to it than that," Berringer said peremptorily. "I am certain that it is wise and necessary to have that policeman at the bedside. I need not tell you that all visitors must be excluded for the present. Why, Sister, it is Tuesday again, is it not? You will be off duty this afternoon and on again this evening, as you were last week."

"I shall be back at five, sir. It is my regular time."

"Then, I must try to arrange to make my visit after tea; if I cannot manage that, I will leave full instructions with your staff nurse."

They saw several more cases together, but these did not erase her feeling that something was amiss with him. Of the two men, she was inclined to think Berringer nearer distraction than his patient, and only conceded to him that it was indeed wise and might yet be necessary to keep some guard over Miles, though she could see no sound basis for her fears.

"I could not be away this afternoon with a clear conscience otherwise," she told herself, and planned her day's shopping without the usual pleasure.

"I shall be leaving at eleven this morning," Hilary told Pounceforth the same day. "I thought I would pay a social call on someone we both know."

"You are not going to see Latimer again! I do not think I can spare you, wherever you are going. You have hardly been in this office for ten consecutive minutes in the last week."

"You were not here for long yourself yesterday," Hilary reminded him. "And I am not going to the nursing home. I thought of having an informal interview with Sidney Berringer."

"I thought you said it was someone we both knew," Pounceforth said easily. "I haven't the pleasure of Berringer's acquaintance, if it can be called a pleasure. I believe he is commonly thought something of a mountebank."

"Why should Pounceforth have sent a skeleton to a man he doesn't know?" Hilary said aloud, but as if to himself. "Pounceforth must know Berringer, though he prefers not to admit it."

Pounceforth got up from his chair and leaned forward with his hands clenched upon the table before him so that the knuckles showed white. "What are you talking about? What fantastic accusation are you making, Scott?"

"It isn't so fantastic or you would hardly be so put out by it. You might be surprised or shocked or even annoyed, but not frightened. And you are frightened, Pounceforth. I don't know why, but I shall make it my business to find out."

"Just one moment. If you leave this office today, I will see to it that you don't come back."

"You forget: I have already resigned my post. Your threat has no substance."

"It has substance, but you misunderstood it," Pounceforth said softly.

"Oh, I see what you mean. There is your telephone. I expect you can get hold of Berringer and tell him that I would be best out of the way, like Miles. Tell him not to bungle the job this time."

"There has been some doubt of Latimer's sanity," Pounceforth said. "Yours will soon be in doubt if you allow yourself to repeat such nonsense."

"You cannot have it both ways. Your threat only makes sense if what I say makes sense too. You should put a curb on your tongue, Pounceforth."

"I should not have thought of taking lessons in discretion from you."

"That's better," Hilary said with approval. "That is your authentic note of venom. Stick to the safer forms of evil-doing, Pounceforth. Keep inside the law and there is very little that will be impossible to a man like you."

They spoke no more; at eleven, Hilary left the room with a curt farewell, and Pounceforth promptly lifted his telephone receiver, only to put it down again. He could not speak to Berringer from this place, thinking it unsafe to allow even the girl on the switchboard to connect their names. Some minutes later at a call box in the nearest post office, he spoke to Berringer's receptionist and learned that her employer was expected back by eleven-thirty. He gave the number of the instrument he was using with an urgent request that Berringer get in touch with him as soon as he arrived. After that he settled down to a harassed perusal of the directory and the instructions for dialling.

"Do you think Mr. Berringer would see me again this morning? You remember I was here yesterday."

"Not unless it is something urgent."

"I thought if he were not booked up——"

"He is always booked up, sometimes for weeks ahead," said the receptionist, who took a sincere if not disinterested pride in her employer's outstanding success.

"Couldn't he spare me five minutes between cases?"

"If this is a social call, come back this afternoon. I can ask him at lunchtime if he will see you then. In the morning he only sees patients."

"I am a patient," Hilary said with determination. "My neck is stiff, I have agonising pain when I turn my head. I couldn't sleep last night. Will that do?"

She looked at him doubtfully. He was personable and she young and unmarried.

"If you like to sit in the waiting room I will have a word with Mr. Berringer when he comes in."

"Are you expecting him soon?"

"At half past eleven. I will let you know what he says, Dr. Scott. It *is* Dr. Scott, isn't it?"

"Yes, that is my name."

She got up and opened a door behind and to the left of her desk. Hilary found himself in a room too well furnished and overoccupied for his purposes, he felt, though, in this, events proved him wrong; five patients were already comfortably arranged upon the cushions. He had no time to be polite: performed a rapid calculation along topographical lines and walked straight through a door in the right-hand wall, in front of five pairs of indignant eyes. "I am in terrible pain," he said over his shoulder with a small, brave smile, and closed the door behind him. He was back, as he had hoped to be, in Berringer's own room. A tall bookcase packed with handsome bindings stood against the opposite wall. There were many large books in it; Hilary's heart sank, looking at them. At least a dozen were large enough to be his quarry and it was probable that none of these was the right one. He had just had time to regret his futile visit when Berringer himself came in through a second door.

"Why, Dr. Scott! Miss Patmore told me you were here but hardly suggested you were already in my room. I have told her I could not see you this morning and I am afraid I must abide by that."

"She told you I needed your professional advice?"

"She said your neck was stiff, yes. I cannot understand why you came in here."

Hilary sat down abruptly on the striped examination couch and buried his head in his hands. "I am an appalling coward, Mr. Berringer. I cannot stand uncertainty. I couldn't have waited in that room, not knowing the truth about my condition."

"What is it you are afraid of, Scott?"

Hilary named a rare and dangerous disease of the cervical spine.

"I can put your mind at ease about that here and now, Scott; take off your jacket and collar. Turn your head to the left. Now to the right. Bend your head. Now straighten it. Is that movement painful? You are pulling a face but you executed it readily enough. Sit down again and let me feel."

Berringer walked round behind the couch and placed his hands gently upon Hilary's throat. His fingers moved up and down in exploration, then slightly tensed.

"There is no muscle spasm here: no glands to be felt, nothing. How long have you had this pain you mention?"

"Ever since I knew that Pounceforth had sent you a skeleton and you had passed it on to Mr. Murivance. It has been worse this morning."

"It will soon be excruciating," Berringer said smoothly and allowed his grasp to tighten.

"There are five patients in your waiting room," Hilary said in a series of gasps, and felt the fingers slacken again. "I am more cautious than Miles Latimer: I have learnt something from his experience."

Berringer withdrew his fingers altogether. "You are talking arrant nonsense, Dr. Scott."

"I think not. I cannot prove anything, but I intend to. And Miles is safe now, as you have probably discovered."

"He is safe now, thanks to my efforts on his behalf. You

should remember that, Scott. If you imply that I intended him to fall, why do you imagine I let him live? Why did I not finish him off while I had the opportunity? You see what an absurdity you suggest!"

"I see only that someone else must have been in the building," Hilary said with interest. "I overlooked that possibility and I suppose you did too."

Berringer tapped crossly upon a table. "Will you leave me now, Scott? You are wasting my time, which is precious."

"More precious than you think. You have not so much left. Pounceforth is almost as nervous as you are. One of you will soon slip up."

The receptionist knocked and entered.

"Dr. Pounceforth has rung again, sir. Oh, Dr. Scott! You shouldn't be in here."

"Don't worry. I have just discovered that for myself. Goodbye, Mr. Berringer. I rather thought that Pounceforth would make the first mistake. You had better see to it that he makes no more."

"It is absolutely essential that I see you," Pounceforth cried from his call box in an agony of impatience.

"Out of the question," Berringer said with great distinctness. "I will get in touch with you later. You should have waited for me to call you back."

"There is a man working in the College, a Dr. Scott——"

"I have met him. He was here when your call was announced."

A prolonged silence followed. Then Pounceforth said in despair, "What are we to do?"

"I wash my hands of the whole matter. You have behaved more than foolishly."

"You are deeper in this than I," Pounceforth snapped.

"Perhaps a little," Berringer said with an eye on his receptionist. "Not enough for you to take any chances. I expect you will be seeing Dr. Scott this afternoon?"

"If he returns to the College. But what can I do? He won't keep quiet at my request; he has never done what I wanted, even in legitimate matters."

"Then, it is up to you to see that he changes his habits. And now I fear I can spare you no more time. I am late for my patients as it is. Goodbye."

Berringer handed the receiver back to the receptionist and she replaced it in its cradle with her usual smile.

"A friend of Dr. Scott's who recommended him to come and see me, and should have told him to make an appointment."

The explanation covered his words, though she had not in fact followed the conversation at all, being busy with correspondence at the time.

Hilary walked down to the front door and closed it loudly behind him in case anyone was listening. Subterfuge was wasted in his case, as in Berringer's. He inspected the names on the unostentatious plates by the bellpull. Mr. Berringer; Dr. Hennessy Jones; Mr. Pratt; Mr. Talbot d'Arcy; Dr. Helga Schlüssel. One to a floor, he observed, and reentering the building quietly, he knocked at Dr. Schlüssel's door, was admitted, announced himself, and asked the receptionist if he could have a word with Dr. Schlüssel.

"She is not here; she is never here on Tuesdays."

"Thank you so much. That is all I wanted to know."

On the first floor, Mr. Talbot d'Arcy was examining a patient and had others to see, was always there on Tues-

days, and often until late in the evening. His secretary examined the appointments book; his last patient the week
before had come at five-thirty. It was possible that he
might still have been in the building an hour later. Hilary
decided to try Mr. Pratt and Dr. Hennessy Jones first; after
he had made certain they were not witnesses to Miles's accident, Mr. Talbot d'Arcy might be able to spare him a
few minutes. But with Mr. Pratt the search came to an
end. The gynaecologist had finished his morning consul-
tations and was dictating his last letter when Hilary was
shown in.

"Certainly I was here last Tuesday night. I shall never
forget it."

"A friend of mine fell from the fourth-floor landing,"
Hilary said, trying not to hope for too much from this interview.

"That poor young man! Berringer tells me he is worse
again now, after some improvement. It is astounding that
he survived at all. Forty feet onto marble blocks! I thought
he would be dead when we found him."

"You found him! You and Berringer!"

"Indeed we did," Pratt said, failing to notice Hilary's rising excitement. "I believe I was first on the scene. We ran
downstairs together, Berringer and I, and I shall never forget my relief when I felt a pulse at the temple. Berringer
was severely shaken; I have never seen him so much at a
loss. I sent him off to ring for an ambulance and stayed
with your friend myself."

"Thank God," Hilary said simply, but did not explain.

"Why have you come to see me, Dr. Scott? Is there anything I can do for you?"

Hilary looked at Pratt and saw a quiet, self-effacing elderly gentleman whose instincts would, he felt sure, ini-

tially prejudice him against Sidney Berringer, as he guessed that Honeychurch's had already done.

"Did you notice anything odd at the time? Please don't wonder why I ask you. It is terribly important to me, and perhaps to my friend as well."

"There was something I didn't quite like," Pratt said after a brief hesitation. "I have mentioned it to no one else. Berringer arranged for your friend's transfer to his nursing home and then went up to fetch some X-ray photographs from his room. He said he could take them with him in the ambulance to save himself an extra journey and it was an ill wind that blew nobody any good. I thought the remark was in poor taste. I can't imagine why I should remember it so clearly. I am afraid you were thinking of something quite different."

"I was not thinking of anything specific," Hilary said slowly. "It is just an idea I had. No, I can't make much of that remark, except that it must have seemed callous."

"Not so much callous as inopportune, I thought."

"But I should have described Berringer as an arch-opportunist," Hilary said to himself, "and looked at in that light, perhaps there is something in it after all, if only I could think what."

Kate and Hilary had lunch together; that is to say, they sat on opposite sides of a table in Schmidt's and watched their food grow cold before them. Hilary could not eat because he was eager to be doing something and could not decide what to do, and Kate's appetite was poor for the same reason that her sleep the previous night had been disturbed and dream-ridden. Her common sense told her that Miles could come to no harm, but some other part of her mind refused to accept this optimistic view, and she knew she would not be happy until he was out of Berringer's nursing home altogether.

"I can't see what to do next, Hilary. There doesn't seem to be anything we can do."

"I've been trying to set a thief to catch a thief. If Pounceforth and Berringer would only destroy each other, there would be nothing more to worry about."

"I wish you would take care of yourself. Berringer is a dangerous man; he seems to stop at nothing. Once Miles is out of the nursing home, surely we can forget the whole thing?"

"You are being parochial, Kate. I am ashamed of you! There was Mr. Murivance as well as Miles, and there might have been me, too. Look."

He loosened his scarf and she exclaimed at the bruises on his neck.

"I have been in the thick of it, as you see. And I don't intend to turn the other cheek. I am full of a desire for vengeance, and it is no longer an altruistic desire, which makes it all the stronger. This afternoon I intend to park my car outside Berringer's rooms. I shall follow him wherever he goes, and keep on following. Sooner or later he will meet Pounceforth, I am sure of it."

"But what good will it do us if he does?" she said doubtfully.

"Don't you see that the link between them, whatever it is, must be something they have to conceal, something criminal, in fact? Once we know it, or suspect it with good enough reason, we can ask for help from the police. Real help, not just someone to keep guard over Miles in wellmeaning ignorance. Imagine bringing the two of them to justice, Kate!"

"I am imagining as hard as I can; but what crime can

Berringer have committed that needs a murder to cover it up? There is nothing worse than murder, nothing that carries a heavier penalty, I mean."

"Then, murder must conceal murder."

"But every murder multiplies the risk."

Hilary shook his head. "I am beginning to know a little about Berringer and he is not a fool; it was safe for him to push Miles, reasonably safe at least. Whatever he did to Mr. Murivance was safe too. It must have been, since we cannot even be certain that anything was done. It would not have been safe to kill me; I reminded him of the fact and he promptly stopped trying. His first murder, the one that has to be concealed, could not have been so safe or the rest would not be necessary. There is some proof of the first one, some concrete detail or other that will give him away. Miles, Mr. Murivance, must both have touched on it."

"But where does Pounceforth come in? Pounceforth seems nearer the heart of the affair than either of the others."

"And is not so innocent. Whatever he knows or suspects, he rates it at its real value. He will take no chances with Berringer."

"That's a pity," Kate said with a certain ruthlessness. "I would have cast him for the role of next victim. There would be a kind of fitness in that."

"I had the same idea, as I was telling you. I tried to suggest to Berringer that Pounceforth was nervous and would make mistakes. And now I am not sure which to watch, except that Berringer has a car, too, and that makes it easier. Pounceforth perhaps goes home to Bayswater on the Inner Circle and might dart off at Baker Street and give me the slip. So it will have to be Berringer."

"I see that now," she said in a small voice, adding as the waiter changed their plates, "if there was something I could do; I am not busy today, Honeychurch will be at the Hospital for Sick Children all the afternoon. I don't want to sit at my desk for three hours trying to make myself believe the work I planned for today is still important."

He saw that she was near to tears and asked for black coffee and brandy, which she drank dutifully but without pleasure.

"Still, it isn't altogether wasted on you. It is to give you Dutch courage; not that you will need it, you have plenty of your own. I want you to go back to the nursing home."

"Of course I will," she said with alacrity. "I was only hoping you would say that."

"Not to see Miles," Hilary explained, "not primarily at least, though I don't see why you shouldn't visit him too while you are there."

"But what am I to do if you didn't mean me to see him?"

"I want you to look at his X-ray films, especially the ones of his leg. Do you know anything about X rays, Kate?"

"A bit; a very little bit," she said ruefully. "I could tell if a bone were broken, I should think. That's what Miles's pictures will show, won't they?"

"Well, yes, I should think they will certainly show that. But they might show something else. I don't know; it is a tiny chance."

"What else, Hilary? What is it all about?"

"I am not sure that the films Miles will have in his room or with his notes or wherever they are will be Miles's X rays at all."

He told her Pratt's story.

"Perhaps there is nothing to it; but if you would like to go and see——"

"Of course I will go!" she cried, and began to pull on her gloves.

He leaned over the table and took her hand. "Not so fast, Kate. If you cannot see anything odd in the pictures yourself, you will have to steal them. Do you think you could do that? Have you a flair for illegal acts, like some of our acquaintance?"

"I am not so practised as Pounceforth," she said with more of a smile than he had seen on her face that day, "but my natural gifts may be greater. And one has to start somewhere; larceny seems to me a very good little crime. Are these X rays going to be large things, Hilary?"

"As large as Miles's leg," Hilary said simply.

She said happily, "Then, it will be quite difficult to do, and I shall have to think of a plan. My afternoon will be better than I dared to hope. If I bring the things away with me, what shall I do with them?"

"Take them back to the College; show them to Prentice. He will remember something from his clinical past, I hope."

They parted outside the restaurant. She would walk to St. John's Wood, she said, and see what ideas came to her on the way. He drove back to Wimpole Street and parked in a side turning. He could see the black Bentley still outside Berringer's door. He made sure there was petrol in his tank and sat back to await his cue.

It took Kate a moment only to convince herself that the X rays were not in Miles's room. She saw Miles, insensible, and the policeman, put out by her intrusion; but there was nothing by the bed except a sheaf of notes of ordinary quarto size and a temperature and prescription chart. The policeman got up and she said quickly, "I am so sorry! I just looked in for a moment. I didn't realise Dr. Latimer would be asleep."

"He is not allowed any visitors now," a voice said behind her, and it was not the sister's voice. Kate turned to meet eyes well below the level of her own, dark round eyes under straight heavy brows. The staff nurse was small, neat, moved rapidly and had a mind of her own. She took an instant dislike to Kate, docketing her arbitrarily as a disturbing influence on the patient: and was confirmed in her impression of the girl's general undesirability by the pallor of her cheeks, the shadows beneath her eyes, and the faint smell of alcohol on her breath. She was severe.

"You should have enquired before you came into this room. This is a nursing home, you know; some discipline is necessary."

Kate said meekly that she was sorry; pushed back her hair with a distracted hand and leaned suddenly and heavily against the doorpost.

"You are not going to faint, are you! Come outside, and sit down quickly. Now put your head down, right down, between your knees. That's better. You will soon be all right. Nurse, bring some water for Miss Cardew. You are Dr. Latimer's fiancée," she said, turning back to Kate in disbelief, for Kate so pale and dishevelled was far from the picture she had made in her mind of the Miss Cardew, so nice, of Sister's description.

Kate accepted the title though she had no right to it, smiled uncertainly and rose to her feet, swaying a little.

"You had better come into the office. You can rest for a bit. It's a pity you came all this way for nothing."

Kate followed the girl slowly, carrying her glass of water

in a hand that seemed to her too steady; she allowed it to shake a little and the water spilled over the carpet. The staff nurse stifled her irritation and indicated a chair.

"Sit there for a few minutes. I'm busy this afternoon, so you will not be in my way. Try to pull yourself together. This sort of foolishness won't do him any good, you know."

She left the room. Kate counted ten slowly, sipping water; she caught sight of herself in a mirror on the wall and thought she could hardly have looked worse if she had really fainted. Then she got up and looked about her. There was a cabinet with rows of shallow drawers by the window; each drawer bore a patient's name and diagnosis. Pulling out the one labelled for Miles, she saw that they contained X-ray films. There was a thick sheaf of them and four typewritten reports. The one on the skull said there was no radiological evidence of fracture at the base or vault. There were two about the wrist: "Colles' type fracture of right wrist: some comminution of the fragments," and "Fracture of right wrist satisfactorily reduced." That on the chest film remarked on three broken ribs and the absence of a pneumothorax or haemothorax. There was no report on the leg. She looked through them again, and still there was nothing about the leg. Her spirits rose. She sorted out the small pictures and the medium-sized ones. That left only the large ones, the films of the femur. There were only two. They had Miles's name on them and the date of the fall and they showed clearly a line of cleavage slanting across the middle of the bone. There was no doubt about it.

"But Hilary said the leg would be broken," she reminded herself. "Anyway I will take them to Prentice and perhaps he will see more in them than I can."

She wore a voluminous coat: between Charlotte Street and St. John's Wood she had equipped herself with a card of safety pins: now she drove the pins with some difficulty through the tough films and secured one to the lining on each side; then drew the coat around her and practised a few steps. There was a rustle but it was hardly noticeable. A step outside the door sent her precipitately back to the cabinet and she closed the drawer just before the staff nurse came in. Kate turned round.

"I was looking at your view."

The staff nurse glanced through the window in some astonishment. The backs of a number of houses had not changed since she had seen them last, and she could not imagine what Miss Cardew could see in them to constitute a view. But Miss Cardew seemed to her a curious, unsympathetic girl, who could be sent on her way now, as she looked better and was anxious to be going.

"You can telephone tonight if you like. Sister will be on duty. But it is no good coming again yet awhile. He probably would not know you if he saw you."

Kate reminded herself that this was only speculation based on faulty premises, as she walked past the staff nurse, smiling stiffly, very conscious of her rustling movement. But her moment of activity was nearly past. She had only, she believed, to deliver the films to Prentice and there would be nothing more for her to do but wait. Wait for Hilary, wait for Miles, wait for Berringer, too, she supposed, and even for Pounceforth. She hated the prospect and hurried back to the College.

"Miss Cardew! To what do I owe this pleasure?"

Prentice was perched on a high stool, examining a specimen with a hand lens. He put the lens back into his pocket to look at Kate, saw at a glance that she was not herself, and slid from his stool with an apology.

"Sit down. Or come into my room and sit down more comfortably. One should not make remarks to a lady about her appearance, but really you don't look at all well."

Prentice was at his best with the suffering, or thought he was, and Kate allowed herself to be fussed over and put into a comfortable chair: but first she took off her coat and before his bewildered mild eyes she unpinned the X-ray films.

"Hilary told me to bring them to you," she said. "He thought there might be something wrong with them."

"Something wrong with them!" Prentice exclaimed, taking the films from her. "Well, of course there is, there is an oblique fracture of the middle third of the right femur. Dr. Scott would have seen that for himself, surely? Oh, I see these are Latimer's X rays. There is his name and the date on the corner. Miss Cardew, I fail to understand how you came by these films."

"There has to be something queer about them," she said hopelessly. "Of course there is the break and Miles's leg is broken. But Hilary thought they might not be his films, all the same."

"Not his films!" Prentice repeated. "Whyever shouldn't they be? Where did you get them from?"

"I stole them," Kate said lightly. "There were comments on the pictures of his skull and wrist and ribs and nothing about these. So I thought these would be the odd ones, if any were. Please, Dr. Prentice, look at them again."

He moved nearer to the window and held first one and then the other up to the light.

"Tell me about them. Talk to me as if I knew nothing, absolutely nothing, about such things. I know very little;

you won't have to exert your imagination so very much. If you were describing them to an ignorant layman, what would you say?"

Prentice struck a pose implying consideration. "This is an antero-posterior view of an adult femur, a trifle over-exposed, but the film is correctly orientated. There is an oblique fracture—"

"I know that," she said with some impatience.

"—an oblique fracture of the middle third with very little displacement of the fragments, a fact confirmed by the lateral view in the second film. Almost certainly such a fracture would unite in good position with simple skin traction using a Thomas splint and a Balkan beam. Of course, I'm not a practising orthopaedist, so I would not like to be too dogmatic on that point. I believe some surgeons prefer skeletal traction even in fractures of this type. Am I boring you?"

"Not boring me. But I don't understand you. What is skeletal traction?"

"It is the term used for drawing the fragments of such a broken bone together and keeping them in line by means of a weight pulling on the lower fragment across the extended knee joint. The surgeon drives a sort of pin through the upper end of the tibia——"

"This is no use," Kate said bitterly. "This can't be what Hilary meant. Miles has a lot of bandages and a splint and a thing over the bed, but nobody has put a pin through his leg."

"That confirms my view. Skin traction, using adhesive strapping and strong bandages would be enough to keep this straight. What is curious, a little perhaps, is the site of the fracture. Now, I would have expected it to be higher up; subtrochanteric or even through the neck. With direct force, of course, one can get a break anywhere, but an old man's bone in a fall is more likely to snap across the neck."

"An old man's bone!" she said with some indignation; "Miles is not old!"

Prentice said patiently, "This is the femur of an elderly man; well past middle age, I would say."

"Think what you are saying!" she cried. "Oh, Prentice, are you sure?"

He looked at her stupidly for a moment and then again at the films. "Of course I am sure. I know a great deal about these things. How did I not see it at first! There are osteoarthritic changes in the hip joint, slight changes even at the knee. And there is narrowing of the bony cortex and generalised osteoporosis."

"Miles is not yet forty," she said. "These are not his films."

"Where are you going?" Prentice asked as she swept up her coat and took the X rays from him.

"To find Honeychurch and tell him what you have told me. And then we can get Miles out of that place. Thank you very much, Dr. Prentice. I am sorry I was impatient, but you see it was important."

He stood in his doorway to watch her go and was sadly puzzled but glad to have been of service to her.

IX

Miles woke with a cry and the policeman sprang to his feet, taken as much by surprise as Miles himself. He moved over to the bed murmuring words he thought might be soothing and was silenced by the look of startled terror on his charge's face; he did not know how closely the look was mirrored on his own.

"He pushed me!" Miles cried out. "I heard him breathing faster and faster. His voice was hoarse and I felt his hand on my back and the wood snapped, and I was falling. Let me go! Let me out of here!"

He pulled himself up in bed and the staff nurse came running, leaving the door to swing.

"Of course you can't go," she told Miles in exasperation. "You are very ill, surely you can understand that? You have had a bad dream, that's all. Now be quiet, please. We can't have you disturbing all the other patients."

He let his head fall back on the pillow; he saw clearly for one shocking second that the nurse was involved in some conspiracy with Berringer; in the next second he doubted his own sanity, for such things cannot happen. Then, with a great effort, he reassembled the pieces of this overwhelming puzzle and said as calmly as he was able, "You are on Berringer's staff. Of course you believe whatever he has told you. It is not your fault if you think I am mad. I can see it would be easier to believe that than to believe he tried to murder me."

It was the girl's turn to react with terror; delusions were outside the range of her nursing experience, and she was more frightened of Miles lying quietly on his bed telling her things that could not be true than she would have been of any phsyical horror. She was out of her depth, and this made her brutal.

"You must not talk like that. Do you want to be put away? That is what happens to people who make silly accusations. Mr. Berringer has done everything for you, and this is all the thanks he gets."

She guessed, Miles knew, that there was more than ingratitude in his outburst; she had only tried to reduce it to familiar terms to keep herself calm. But what she had said seemed to him, strung up as he was, simply funny. He laughed, and the laugh sent her flying out of the room, convinced that he was dangerous and only thankful that he could not be more so. She was speaking to Berringer on the telephone within five minutes.

"He is saying the most dreadful things. I know I should not worry you with them, but it is too much for me! Sister would know what to do, but she won't be back for another hour. I thought of giving him some more hyoscine."

"No," Berringer said peremptorily. "I will come myself. You need not shoulder any more responsibility; it would not be fair. Is he shouting? Is he violent? What is happening at this moment?"

"He is talking to the policeman," she said, after listening at the door of the sister's office for a few seconds.

"I will come at once. There is nothing to worry about." He rang off.

The policeman patted Miles's hand.

"Look, I am as sane as you are. How can I convince you? Ask me the day of the week, the month of the year, who won the Ashes. I can tell you it all. I tell you Sidney Berringer pushed me over a balustrade."

"You shouldn't say such things, Doctor. You saw how it upset nurse. Why should Mr. Berringer do a thing like that?"

"How should I know why? I never saw him before that day."

"You see!" the policeman said triumphantly. "It's just a funny idea you've got into your head. Not that it's surprising, with all the damage you did yourself. Anybody would be a bit queer after a fall like that."

"I have been queer enough," Miles said, "and now I am normal again. I know what happened. I am not guessing or wondering any longer. I remember it moment by moment." He said in despair, "Why should I make up such a thing if it did not happen?"

"Of course it happened," the policeman said in a consoling tone, recalling too late that lunatics are to be humoured. "If you say you were pushed, pushed you were. Now try to go to sleep again, Doctor. You were much better off asleep."

"He has kept me drugged for days," Miles said, shaking with an impotent rage. "Can't you understand that? I had to be kept quiet in case I remembered."

"Of course you did. Everything is just as you say. Try not to get all hot and bothered about it. It won't do you a bit of good."

Miles put a hand over his eyes; his mouth twisted suddenly like that of a child about to cry. When he lifted his hand, his eyes were still in shadow. Berringer stood between him and the light.

"What are you upsetting yourself about, Latimer? What is all this I hear?"

"You tried to murder me," Miles said with great distinctness. "Nobody else will believe what I say, but you believe it. You and I know that it is true."

"This is very bad," Berringer said, but not to his patient. "This is a fearful change. I don't know that we can keep him here. Our nurses are not used to dealing with the mentally deranged."

"Send me where you like!" Miles cried, on a swift uprush of hope. "Anywhere would be better than here."

Berringer looked down at him compassionately, earning himself glances of the deepest respect from the policeman and the staff nurse.

"My poor fellow! Of course I will not send you away. You know how deeply responsible I feel for everything that has happened to you. It may surprise you to hear," he told them all, "that *I* have sometimes felt myself almost a murderer over this affair. If I had never suggested that he should look closely at my balustrade——"

"If you had never come up behind me," Miles said, with the persistence of a man driven beyond fear, "if you had never pushed me over, there would be no need for you to feel so deeply responsible."

"Why do you imagine I did such a thing?" Berringer said, being in a different way every bit as desperate as Miles.

"I don't know," Miles said. "That is the only thing I can't remember, if I ever knew it."

Berringer's look included his audience in a personal triumph. "Believe me, Latimer, this is only a sort of waking nightmare. It will pass, as all such things do. We will talk no more of insanity or derangement or anything so horrible. We will just say that you have suffered a great deal and had better suffer no more. Nurse!"

They moved away and spoke for a moment in the doorway. She went in search of a syringe and needles. Miles said to the policeman, "You are an accessory before and after the fact. You may even be an accomplice before this thing is ended, and you will have it that way. I can see that it isn't your fault. Remember what I am saying; it is quite likely that these are my last words."

But his philosophical calm broke down when Berringer approached him with a syringe already filled.

"Shut the door, Nurse. There is no reason why my other patients should have their feelings harrowed. Now hold his free ankle." To the policeman he said, "Put your hand over his mouth and keep his left hand out my way. The other does not matter."

"I wonder what he thought I had in my syringe?" Berringer said in an amused way a few seconds later. "It was only hyoscine, Latimer. There was nothing to be afraid of."

Miles turned his head away on the damp pillow, but could not stop himself trembling. Words seemed futile; he thought of Kate and touched the fringes of a vast desolation.

The nurse said briskly, having recovered confidence with useful activity, "Sister will be back at five, Mr. Berringer. Shall I give her any message?"

"Oh, I don't think you need say anything more than your ordinary report will cover. I don't imagine our friend here will give her any further trouble."

"You think he will be quite reasonable when he comes round from this injection, sir?"

"Well, that's not quite what I said, is it? I believe your

worries over Dr. Latimer are past. We had better leave it at that."

The room was quite dark. Sister came in and put her hand on the light switch; then she thought better of it and crossed to the bed in the path of illumination from the door.

"You are not asleep!" she said in surprise.

"No. It was not hyoscine, you see. I knew it wasn't, and now I have only to try to guess what it was."

"You have been trying to keep awake, and the hyoscine has only made you excited. You know that can happen if one fights against a narcotic."

"But I am not excited. You can see I am not."

"Of course it was hyoscine," she argued, but it was herself she was trying to convince. She had received the staff nurse's report in a kind of stupefaction: nothing in her years of nursing had prepared her for this. "Has he been restless?" she demanded of the policeman, sitting faithfully in the shadows.

"No, Sister, I can't say that he has, exactly. Breathing a bit hard and shivering sometimes, but not what you would call restless."

She thought quickly, went back to the door, and switched on the light.

"If I can find the empty ampoule, will that convince you, Dr. Latimer?"

"You speak as if it were worth convincing me," Miles said with sudden hope. "At least *you* don't believe I am mad, deluded?"

"Of course you are not mad," she said sharply, speaking from her intuition as well as her sound clinical knowledge. "It shouldn't surprise anyone if your ideas are mixed after all the sedatives you have been given. The wonder is that you can think at all."

She left the room and went in search of a junior nurse who had been on duty all the afternoon.

"Who prepared Mr. Berringer's tray for the injection?"

"Staff Nurse, Sister."

"And did she bring it out to the sluice?"

"She rinsed it through and put it in the steriliser herself, Sister."

"Did you see the ampoule that was used? Did you notice it on the tray when she was in the sluice?"

The nurse thought a moment.

"No, Sister. I don't remember seeing anything but the syringe and two or three needles and a bit of gauze. But Staff Nurse might have dropped it in the wastepaper basket."

"I want you to look through the dirty-dressing bin, Nurse, and see if you can find that ampoule. It is vitally important or I would not ask you to do such a thing. Use forceps. I will look in the wastepaper baskets, though I cannot imagine Staff Nurse would be so slipshod."

There was no broken ampoule in the basket, and the three that were retrieved from among the dirty dressings bore other labels and could be easily accounted for. Sister went into her office and closed the door. Then she dialled the number of the Nurses' Homes and spoke to her staff nurse.

"Of course there was an ampoule, Sister. Mr. Berringer brought it with him. I had told him over the telephone that Dr. Latimer was out of his mind, so he came prepared."

Sister said, "Did you look at the label?"

The hesitation told her all she required to know.

"I did not load the syringe, Sister. Mr. Berringer did it himself, and of course I did not think it necessary to check the dose for him."

"It is probably more necessary with Mr. Berringer," Sister said sadly, "than with any other member of his profession. But it would have been difficult for you, I can see that."

She put down the receiver and went back to Miles.

"I can't show you the ampoule. Mr. Berringer brought it himself and must have taken it away again. Shall I send for the police?"

"We have the police already," Miles said dryly. "I don't know that it would help much to augment our supply. It might be better to send for Professor Honeychurch." After a fraction of a moment's pause, he added, "and Kate, too, if it is not too much trouble to find her?"

"I thought it would be adrenaline," he said to Honeychurch fifteen minutes later. "But of course adrenaline was Pounceforth's idea. Whatever Berringer gave Mr. Murivance, it can't have been that. It would have taken him half an hour at least to get back to the College: so it was something that acted slowly. And I am still alive after nearly two hours, so it must be even slower than that."

Kate caught her breath, stood up, and walked over to the window.

"How do you feel?" Honeychurch asked, lowering himself into the chair she had vacated. "Have you any symptoms? Your skin feels damp."

"That is only fear," Miles said candidly. "My pulse is rapid, for the same reason. No, I have waited for a dry mouth, tingling fingers, cramps in the legs, and nothing happens. Perhaps this is an elaborate joke on Berringer's part. Or perhaps he would like me really to become insane."

Honeychurch demanded a diagnostic tray and a pair of scissors. He cut through the bandages holding Miles's leg on the splint with resolution: the counterweights fell to the floor with a resounding crash.

"What are you doing?" Miles said, pulling himself up in the bed to watch.

"It is not broken; it was never broken. We know that now, thanks to Kate and Dr. Prentice. Berringer passed off some films of another patient as yours. He must have had them in his rooms; he cut off the name and substituted your own. Kate and Prentice brought them to me, and when we measured them against another film of standard size, there was a half-inch strip missing from the top. He must have thought you were safer immobile and in his charge. Now I am going to examine you thoroughly, and then we will decide what to do."

Ten minutes passed. Sister led Kate away to her office and had tea made for her. When they had gone, Miles said with difficulty, "I should never have asked for her to come. This isn't a thing she should have to remember."

"She was in the room when I spoke to Sister on the telephone," Honeychurch said, pausing for a moment with his ophthalmoscope in midair. "I could not have kept her away. Of course she had to come. Later you will share the memory and exorcise it together. No, I can find no physical signs. There is nothing special about the site of injection."

Miles's lips framed a question.

"We shall have to find Berringer. That is the obvious thing to do. I have a friend who can help us. And you must be moved to another place; somewhere where they can deal promptly with anything that arises. I will send Kate in to you and arrange for an ambulance."

"To leave this room! An hour ago I believed I never would, not alive. Well, it's something to have achieved that much."

"That is the spirit," Honeychurch said eagerly. "I will tell you now, Hilary is already following Berringer. We don't know where Hilary is, but he will get in touch with us. So you see there is hope, plenty of hope."

"And I am hungry," Miles said in surprise. "I believe I have had nothing to eat all day."

"It could do you no harm to have a little food. I will ask Sister to have something sent in to you."

He was as good as his word and in a short time Miles and Kate were drinking tea together and sharing a plate of biscuits: Kate eating only because she wanted to conceal her dread, Miles ravenously as if a week's starvation rather than a day's preceded this meal. Honeychurch, closing the door on them, shook a puzzled head. Then he went to see a physician of his acquaintance, a much-respected man who had beds at two teaching hospitals and many brilliant young men only too eager to watch over an interesting case under his benign supervision. Within an hour Miles was in a side ward at St. Chad's telling his story as coherently as it could be told. Honeychurch and the physician nodded at each other over the bed; a sudden idea came to Honeychurch belatedly but with great clarity.

"Why did you go to see Berringer in the first place, Miles?"

"To take him back his book," Miles said promptly.

"What book was that?"

"The one he had lent Mr. Murivance; about Roman remains in Britain. I can't recall the title or the author."

"So that is it," Honeychurch said happily. "Berringer and Pounceforth and you and Mr. Murivance and that place in Hertfordshire where Pounceforth goes digging at the weekend, instead of cultivating his own garden like an honest man. Now I think we might usefully call in the police. We were a little premature last night."

Kate waited outside the room.

"We shall catch Berringer, my dear, never fear. We know most of the story now, and soon we shall know it all."

"I only want to know what he has done to Miles. Will he tell you, if he is caught? Supposing it is too late!"

Honeychurch could offer her no easy comfort; instead he went to the telephone and called Inspector Burnivel of the Criminal Investigation Department, who was also a friend of his, if not a close one. Burnivel listened to his story, punctuating it with interruptions, some of which were queries, some outright protests.

Finally he said, "It sounds a lot of rubbish to me. I'll come along and see you when I can get away."

With that, Honeychurch had to be content.

X

Shortly after two, Berringer left his consulting rooms, climbed into his car and drove off. Hilary followed at a discreet distance. It was not, he soon discovered, as easy a task to follow a car through a crowded city in the daytime as the cinema had led him to believe. It was as well he had some idea of where his quarry was likely to be going. They visited St. John's Wood briefly: Hilary waited outside while Berringer administered the drug of his choice to Hilary's friend. Then they set off again, the one feeling more secure for his recent action, the other comfortably assured that all must be well within the nursing home. Berringer was consulting orthopaedic surgeon to a number of hospitals, and his route southwards across Oxford Street suggested that he might be making for St. Jude's. Hilary lost the trail at Hyde Park Corner but decided to back his fancy, and was rewarded ten minutes later with the sight of the Bentley parked and empty in the formal courtyard of the second-oldest of the London teaching hospitals. He parked his own car with a friendly nod to the beadle; and on second thoughts went over to speak to the man.

"Is that Mr. Berringer's car?"

"Yes, sir. It is his Outpatient Clinic this afternoon."

"Could you tell me what time he is likely to be finished?"

"Not before four, sir. Perhaps not much before five. It varies with the number of patients."

"I suppose it does."

"Did you want to see him, sir, or leave a message?"

Hilary said on impulse, "If you would let him know that Dr. Pounceforth has been enquiring for him—?"

"I will see what can be done, sir."

The message, relayed by no less than three intermediaries, reached Berringer as he was examining his fifth patient.

"Has been enquiring for me? What does that mean, has been enquiring for me?"

"He spoke to the beadle in the courtyard, sir."

"Then, the beadle in the courtyard must tell him I am not to be disturbed during my clinics. I will see Dr. Pounceforth later, as I have promised."

Hilary said casually to the beadle, "Tell Mr. Berringer I will meet him outside the gates here at half past four. Or perhaps at five. That will give him a little extra time."

The beadle dispatched the second message with misgivings and pocketed a suitable coin. There was no reply this time. Hilary left his car and walked into the medical school on the far side of the courtyard. He tapped upon a glass door labelled "Office" and wandered in. A clerk glanced up.

"I hope I have come to the right place. Mr. Berringer sent me over with a message. He wanted somebody to call the Royal College of Paediatricians for him. Could you do that?"

She smiled and nodded and invited him to take a seat. "It is for a Dr. Pounceforth. An odd name."

She agreed and dialled a number. "Dr. Pounceforth? There is somebody here to speak to you."

"I don't want to speak to him myself," Hilary said hastily. "If you would just tell him that Mr. Berringer will meet him outside the main gates of St. Jude's at five this evening."

She did what he asked. "Dr. Pounceforth seemed rather surprised," she remarked a moment later, putting the receiver down.

"Surprised and pleased?"

"Well, perhaps pleased."

"They should have a lot to say to each other," Hilary said cheerfully. "Thank you for helping me to bring them together."

She was still wondering about this when the office door closed behind him.

Of course, Hilary could not get close enough to them to hear what they were saying. He stayed in his car and watched them walking up and down under the plane trees, ten steps one way, ten steps the other. He could see that Berringer was furious: each time he passed beneath the lighted lamp over the gate, his large face was creased into lines of incredulity and rage. Pounceforth's mood was less constant. He had seemed jaunty and even impudent on his arrival, but his step as he moved along at Berringer's side became less certain with every turn, and soon the movements of his hands began to suggest deprecation, apology. Then one or the other must have said something decisive: they separated, as if jerked apart on wires. Pounceforth's head went back and his lips parted in a caricature of his usual smile. Berringer opened the door of the Bentley and thrust his attaché case inside with a vivid gesture of finality.

Hilary lowered the window of his car and called softly,

"Do you want a lift, Pounceforth? Can I take you some-where?"

"How did you get here, Scott?" Pounceforth cried in a snapping tone of disbelief. "Certainly you can take me somewhere. Follow Sidney Berringer, if you want to get to the bottom of this business."

"I will do what I can," Hilary promised. "Have you discovered how nasty and unreliable your friend is? You cannot touch pitch and not be defiled. You had better wash your hands of the whole affair."

"So it was *you*," Pounceforth said thoughtfully. "It was you who engineered this meeting. I might have known."

"Hurry up if you want to come with me. He is starting up and I dare not let him get too far ahead; his car is much more powerful than mine. You still want to follow him?"

"Of course I do. What are you trying to do, Scott?" Pounceforth added with indignation as Hilary took hold of his arm.

"Get you inside my car. Surely that is obvious! Look, he is already turning——"

Pounceforth got in beside Hilary and slammed the door.

"Where is he going?" Hilary demanded.

"To Throckleford," Pounceforth said, thinking fast. "Get back to the Edgware Road. We can turn off past Hemel Hempstead."

"Throckleford?" Hilary pondered over this, but it meant nothing to him, since he read his newspaper in a highly selective manner and the selection did not embrace antiquarian enthusiasms. To ask more questions would be to reveal the paucity of his knowledge to Pounceforth, and it seemed wise to keep Pounceforth in ignorance on that point. His companion seemed uncertain; his readiness to accept Hilary as a possible ally suggested a radical split with Berringer, and Berringer was in no mood to act calmly. It was fair to assume that their next meeting might end in violence, Berringer being the man he was. Hilary intended to hear what passed between them this time, even if he had to pay for his presence by helping Pounceforth to escape his deserts.

The night was dark, still, and bitterly cold, the streets thickly lined with people, the Edgware Road a string of lights, the Aylesbury Road beyond Abbot's Langley full of powerful cars carrying their drivers far enough from the city for them to make believe they were living in the depths of the country. Pounceforth was silent and assented with a bare nod when Hilary turned north through Boxmoor and began to climb towards Berkhamsted Common. They passed Ashridge: two or three miles further on they saw the Bentley again, stationary at the roadside.

"He came here! I knew he would!" Pounceforth said. "Drive further on, Scott. He will hear us if you stop now. We can walk back."

Hilary stopped the car on the outskirts of the village. "There is a pub. I think we had better go in for a moment."

"You want to waste time drinking, now?"

"No. I was thinking of using their telephone. I would like Honeychurch to know where I am if I am going to explore rural Hertfordshire in your company, Pounceforth. Forgive me if that sounds offensive."

"I am not offended," Pounceforth said smoothly. "Do as you think best. But it might be better not to waste any more time. Trunk calls are long-drawn-out affairs, and Honeychurch is sometimes difficult to find."

"And I have no small change," Hilary said with a sudden feeling of lightheadedness. "Of course the people in the bar would have some, but your other reasons still hold. Well, let's take this trick ourselves. We have earned it; I have, anyway."

They walked back in silence. Opposite a clump of trees, Pounceforth made a sudden turn off the road: the sound of his tread on dead bracken brought him to a standstill at once.

"To get into the wood, we have to cross this ground," he told Hilary, stationary at the roadside, "unless we make a long detour. And I don't think it wise to leave him alone there any longer than we must."

"If we walk on this stuff, Berringer will be out of the wood before we are ten yards nearer it."

"Not if you tread carefully. I have been here often and it will not take many minutes."

Hilary walked with extreme caution, taking advantage of tiny islands of turf and a brief twisting path that appeared suddenly before him and came as suddenly to an end. Then he realised that his wariness was going for nothing. Pounceforth was capering over the rustling carpet of fronds like a March hare. Hilary swore at him.

"Do you want Berringer to know that we are coming?"

"Well, it hardly matters, Scott. He will be expecting us some time or other and now is as good as any."

Hilary came to an abrupt halt. "Expecting us! What do you mean?"

"I have an appointment with him," Pounceforth said with an odd, raucous chuckle.

"In a place like this! You must be mad. Surely you know how dangerous he is?"

"Nobody knows better than I," Pounceforth admitted. "When I received his summons—your summons, Scott, I should say—I made the arrangements I thought suitable. I unpacked my service revolver and loaded it. Here it is."

"Good for you," Hilary said with approval.

"It was so fortunate that you were able to give me a lift in your car. Otherwise I should have experienced some little difficulty in getting here."

Pounceforth laughed again, a high-pitched laugh that reminded Hilary briefly of Mr. Murivance's irritating giggle, and added in great good humour, "Why do you not ask the obvious question, Scott? Surely it has occurred to you? You are intelligent enough, or so they tell me."

Hilary said, suddenly noticing how cold it was, "Why did you not come with Berringer?"

"Yes, that is the question I meant. It is strange that I should be afraid to travel with him and not afraid to meet him here. And another question; there is another as obvious as the first."

"How were you going to get here at all?"

"You are thinking remarkably quickly," Pounceforth said. Hilary had never seen him so pleasant, so ungrudging. "You were going to bring me; or to put it another way, I was going to bring you."

They stood not three feet apart, absurdly facing each other; and the gun which had been lying slackly in Pounceforth's neatly gloved hand was now pointing at Hilary.

"It is you who must be mad, Scott. It is you who take risks. You brought Berringer and myself together. No doubt you imagined sparks would fly at our meeting. So they did, other sparks than those you planned. We share a common danger, and there is nothing so well calculated to make people forget their personal differences. You were our common danger. Berringer suggested that I should get you to drive me out here. I was to use whatever means were needed to persuade you: as it happened, you persuaded me instead. No subtle tactics were necessary on my part. Here you are, as you see. Curiosity proverbially killed the cat and will very likely kill you also."

"Then, there is nothing here?" Hilary said, almost more conscious of disappointment than of fear. "This is only a place you chose at random for disposing of me?"

"I didn't say that. Berringer is revisiting the scene of his crime. It sounds such a stupid thing to do, and in his case it is quite pointless. I wonder if he knows that yet?"

"I hate your laugh," Hilary said.

"I suppose the situation hardly seems comical to you," Pounceforth said as if granting a concession, "but it has elements of humour all the same. Berringer anticipated a longer start than he has got. He is trying to destroy the evidence; or perhaps he has found by now that there is no evidence left to destroy. Let us go into the wood, Scott. You will walk just in front of me. I am not a good shot, but I can hardly miss at this range."

Hilary did what he was told, not seeing any alternative for the moment. He was also as curious as Pounceforth surmised. It would give him a definite if tenuous satisfaction to get to the root of the affair before Pounceforth squeezed the trigger.

Berringer leaned upon his spade and panted rhythmically. He was unused to extreme physical exertion, and the sensation of a silk shirt clinging damply to his body was one he had met only in the calmer context of the operating theatre. To dig at all was a penance, if only a little one. To dig deeper and deeper and to find nothing under the loose soil but more loose soil was to touch a genuine mortification. "If only I had not" is only a step removed from confession and atonement, but it is a big step, and Berringer was not in a frame of mind to take it. He flung his spade away with a deep sound of despair, and in the quiet that followed its crashing flight into the undergrowth he heard Hilary and Pounceforth approaching. He came out of the wood at once. There was a larger moon than he had had a week before to illuminate this wood, and in the full but subdued light his face and Hilary's were drained of colour, Pounceforth's rosy cheeks looked black and hollow. Berringer steadied himself with a hand against a tree and looked at them both in purest loathing.

"What have you done?"

"I have brought Scott here, as I promised," Pounceforth said with imperturbable calm.

"What have you done?" Berringer repeated more loudly. "You know what I mean. Don't pretend that you don't."

"There is no need to be so secretive. You have no secrets from me and Scott will not pass on what he hears tonight. Will you, Scott?"

Hilary said nothing, preferring to listen.

"What have you done with her?" Berringer demanded, but his bullying tone was without the necessary undernote of confidence.

"I buried her elsewhere," Pounceforth said. "You threw down my spade and I picked it up. The earth was loose, as you left it; the task was easy. I am more practised at digging than you are. I advise you to take up archaeology, Berringer. It is profitable, I have found, as well as pleasant. It gets you out into the fresh air and develops the muscles."

"But why, why?"

"Because I am not a fool," Pounceforth snapped. "You

came here tonight with a spade; I can see the handle of it among those brambles. You might have come here before. If I were to get any reward for my exemplary silence on these matters I could not risk your taking away the proof of your act. So I took it away myself. I could lead my fellow archaeologists to a body; you would hardly be in a position to object that it had been moved in your absence."

Berringer was peculiarly silent.

"I think you had better accept my terms," Pounceforth said, on a note of condolence. "I doubt if you could ask for better in the circumstances."

"I would use more tact with Berringer if I were you," Hilary remarked, hoping that he sounded more disinterested than he felt. "Remember that you will shortly be alone with him. He is not a person I care to be alone with. Five minutes with him today convinced me of that, and I knew that there was help at hand, a comfort you will have to forgo after I leave you. He has two murders and two attempts at murder to his credit, and it may be that the habit of killing is growing on him."

"You underestimate me, Dr. Scott. The score has risen to three, or will do so shortly."

"Pounceforth has already told me that I shall not come out of this place alive."

"That is not what I mean."

For some interminable moments no one spoke.

"What have you done to him?" Hilary said at last in a strained voice. "What can you have done? We thought we had made him safe——"

"There is no point in my answering your questions. It is nearly seven now and he will be dead before midnight; so you see he was not safe after all."

"Whatever you did to Mr. Murivance you have done to Miles, too."

"Substantially. A smaller dose for Murivance, because he was older. And I am not going to gratify your curiosity, Scott. I see no reason why you should die happy. Your friend will not."

The policeman out of whose charge Miles had so unceremoniously been swept reported the matter instantly to his superior. The superior, less confused than the man on the spot by what could be guessed at of Miles's affairs and Berringer's, saw his duty with a blessed clarity and got in touch with the Duly Authorised Officer. At the moment when Berringer determined to shatter Hilary's insouciance with the revelation of his latest homicidal exploit, the Duly Authorised Officer knocked on the door of Miles's room at the hospital and was admitted by a nurse. Within were the patient, his patient; Professor Honeychurch, on whose behalf he had acted at some cost to himself in time and trouble; the celebrated physician of whose existence and fame he was equally unaware; and the young woman whose importunity, added to that of the Professor, had brought his authority into full play.

"I should like to know the meaning of this!" he exclaimed in bitterness and wrath. "Last night you appealed to me to protect this man against himself. Today you take him away without so much as a word to me. What sort of game do you think you are playing?"

"It is not exactly a game," Honeychurch said carefully, silencing his eminent colleague with a gentle nod. "We misled you a little last night, I fear, in suggesting that it was Dr. Latimer's own idea to take his life."

"Misled me!" the Duly Authorised Officer said blankly.

"You deliberately gave me to understand that your friend here had had one shot at killing himself. You told me he was likely to try it again even when he was all strung up on that overhead splint thing. Now here he is, wide awake and free as air, and you think you can just whisk me away with a wave of your hand. Let me tell you you're quite wrong about that. Look at the man now. Obviously he's not normal."

Kate, Honeychurch, the physician, obediently looked at Miles, who lay with his eyes open, pulling at the bedclothes and murmuring under his breath. His face shone with sweat; an artery at his temple shook with the racing pulse. Whatever he said came spasmodically in great stammering bursts too low for the words to be made out.

Honeychurch said explicitly, "He is certainly not normal, but that is not to say he is insane. He has been poisoned."

"Poisoned! What with? Who by?"

"By Sidney Berringer. We don't know what with. He cannot tell us."

"He told you Mr. Berringer poisoned him!" said the Duly Authorised Officer, adding in a tone of wonder, "And you think he is not mad! Doesn't it strike you that the man has been having hallucinations?"

"You think this is an acute paranoid schizophrenia?" the eminent physician asked, suddenly emerging from an apparent torpor.

"Of course that is what it is. He has his friends here completely flummoxed. Are you one of his friends, sir?"

"I never saw him before tonight. And I must say, Fabian, that if it were not for all you have told me I should be much inclined to agree with the officer here. Latimer is certainly raving now, whatever he was before."

"He is not raving," Kate said suddenly and passionately. "Not in the sense you mean. Something has done this to him, and all we can do is stand here and argue whether or not he is mad. What does it matter? It is all the effect of whatever Berringer gave him. We know that, don't we?" She turned to Honeychurch in appeal.

"I didn't wish to upset the young lady. This can't be very nice for her when all is said and done. But there is no need to stand here and argue, as she puts it. I have brought a constable with me and with your permission, sir"—the Duly Authorised Officer picked out the physician as a likely ally—"we can get him into a mental observation ward at once. If the professor likes to stay with him, I don't imagine there will be any objection."

"That sounds an entirely sensible notion," the eminent physician said with enthusiasm. "Honeychurch, surely you can have no objection to that? If you can name me one drug that produces an effect like this, I will keep your friend here; but if not, I really think we should assume that he is suffering from delusions of persecution and has succeeded in deluding you into the bargain."

"He has done nothing of the sort!" Honeychurch said angrily. "I am sure it would be unwise to move him again. You will admit that he is ill, very ill?"

"Certainly he is. But he need not leave the building. We have a small observation ward of our own next to the casualty department. If the officer agrees, he could be transferred in a matter of minutes."

"That would meet my case very satisfactorily," said the Duly Authorised Officer.

Kate turned her head away, and her eyes filled with tears.

"After all," the physician said in a kind, subdued voice,

"it is only a matter of prejudice, is it not? There is so much that can be done these days; psychiatry does not stand still, any more than medicine does."

"Certainly it doesn't," the Duly Authorised Officer said, offering Kate untimely condolences. "What with modern treatment, electroconvulsion therapy, insulin shock, leucotomies, you know, in a few cases——"

"Not in this case," Honeychurch said. "Kate, my dear, don't be alarmed at all this nonsense. Insulin shock, indeed!"

But a moment later, "Insulin shock!" he repeated thoughtfully. "Rupert, can you rustle me up some 20 percent glucose and a syringe, and someone to do a blood sugar for me?"

Kate glanced up in new and wondering hope.

"Fabian, you are surely not suggesting that this man has been given insulin? It is four hours since he had the injection you spoke of. With a massive dose of insulin he would have been comatose within the hour."

"Look at him!" Honeychurch said. "Look at him without bias. Tell me if that isn't the very picture of incipient insulin coma."

"But it is too late," said the eminent physician. "Too late by hours. An insulin coma not only starts soon but comes on rapidly. This is a slow business; it is unfolding before our eyes. The other would have been over in a flash."

"Do not waste time on words, Rupert. Get me a pathologist and I believe I can prove my point. I would almost swear it, but I am not given to swearing."

A pathologist was summoned, drew blood, retired. As soon as he left, Honeychurch drove a large quantity of glu-

cose solution into a vein on the back of Miles's sound
wrist. Kate waited as if for a miracle and Honeychurch
shook his head.

"Do not expect anything dramatic. It has taken time for
this thing to take effect and it will take time for the effect
to wear off with treatment. If somebody could prepare a
fair-sized meal with sweetened tea to follow?" he suggested
to the eminent physician.

Half an hour later, the physician shook Honeychurch's
hand with a certain solemnity. "You were right, though I
fail to see how you could have been. His blood sugar was
down to thirty-five. Now explain this, please."

Honeychurch said simply, "It is a thing you do every day,
Rupert; or your diabetic patients do it for you. Ordinary
insulin is not much used these days, once the condition is
under control. You prescribe a long-acting form of insulin,
do you not? The patient can manage with only one or two
injections each day, because these drugs act slowly and act
for a long time. It is a matter of great convenience in the
treatment of diabetes, and it was nearly as convenient for
Sidney Berringer. There was no risk of his method being
detected, for insulin is always present in the tissues; there
was no chance of his victim dying so soon after the injection as to make the injection itself seem suspicious. He
gave globin insulin to Theodore Murivance instead of procaine while he was treating his shoulder, and he gave it
to Miles this afternoon: and no doubt expected him to be
dead by midnight with nothing to show for it and nobody
being much surprised, since head injuries are known to
take unpredictable courses. Our glucose will counteract
most of the action of the insulin; a good meal will keep his
blood sugar up until the effect of the drug passes off. I

wish I had guessed why he was hungry before; then he might have had more to eat while he was still able to take it."

"There is somebody to see Professor Honeychurch," a nurse announced.

Honeychurch left the room with a backward glance at Miles, quiet now, and Kate quiet too in her absolute relief. Inspector Burnivel, a dark, neat, forceful man in a dark neat overcoat, was waiting for him outside the door.

"So you really have a bit of a case," he said when Honeychurch had told him the most recent developments. "Where's this man Berringer now? I ought to be able to get a warrant out for him on the strength of what you have told me."

"I don't know. A young man called Scott is keeping an eye on him, but I fear I have lost touch with Scott."

"Supposing we don't find him at his home or his consulting rooms or anywhere obvious like that, we'll try the Throckleford place next. It sounds as if there might be something there that would interest us."

"I doubt if the remains will be entirely Roman," Honeychurch agreed. And added, his heart suddenly misgiving him as he thought of Hilary, "I only hope they are not *too* recent."

Hilary said, "It is a small point, but which of you is going to shoot me?"

"It is Pounceforth who has the gun," Berringer said.

"Berringer is evasive," Hilary said to Pounceforth. "Will you give me a straight answer to a straight question?"

Pounceforth was more evasive still, remaining silent.

"Let us get it over, Pounceforth," Berringer said shortly. "Remember, our work here does not end with that."

"Of course it does not," Hilary agreed. "How fortunate that there are two of you to do the digging this time. Or have you only one spade between you? That will slow you down."

"Talk as much as you like," Pounceforth said. "Talk will not get you out of this."

"Nothing else will," Hilary remarked with a glance at the revolver. "I am saying whatever nonsense comes into my head in order to distract your attention from the ten uniformed policemen advancing over the bracken."

Berringer turned immediately towards the mosaic pavement and the road beyond it: Pounceforth only moved nearer to Hilary and pressed the muzzle of his gun against his ribs.

"Nobody is coming," Hilary said impatiently. "Berringer, you are not nearly as competent a criminal as you think. Even Pounceforth knew better than to believe me! You are both hopelessly amateur, and the only difference between you is that Berringer has tasted blood and Pounceforth hasn't. Now is your chance, Pounceforth."

"Why don't you run, Scott?" Pounceforth asked in a silky voice. "I could shoot you in the back. I have told you I am not a good shot."

"Then, let Berringer do it. I hate to fuss over trivial matters, but this is not so trivial to me. I feel sure that Berringer would shoot well; he is a man who makes the most of his opportunities."

"Give me that gun," Berringer said brusquely. "We cannot stand here forever."

"Of course we cannot, it is far too cold. That is why I am shivering. I should hate you to think there was any other reason."

Berringer moved nearer to Pounceforth with his hand

outstretched and Hilary said swiftly, "Be careful, Pounce-forth. I have already told you it is risky to be alone with Berringer. It will be riskier still if he has your gun. As long as it is in your hand, you are safe enough."

"There is something in what you say," Pounceforth said slowly. "Stand back, Berringer. This is your time to learn who is master of the situation."

"That's better," Hilary said, leaning carefully against a tree, since his legs seemed less useful to him at this juncture than his active brain. "For a short time at least you may as well cast yourself as first murderer, Pounceforth. You have some of the qualities of greatness after all. The power of making rapid decisions, for one. The choice between wealth and personal safety must have been difficult to make: I think you have chosen wisely."

Pounceforth looked sidelong at Berringer; Berringer was smiling a broad, almost ingenuous smile.

"What are you trying to say, Scott?"

"If you give Berringer the gun he will shoot us both, first one and then the other; the order is irrelevant. If you kill me yourself, you will never get a penny out of him. You are buying your life at the expense of whatever he was going to pay you."

Berringer continued to smile. "Scott is perfectly right, Pounceforth."

Pounceforth looked from one to the other, his gaze so blank that Hilary laughed outright, hoping they would not observe how near he was to hysteria.

"Do you think you will be able to blackmail Berringer once he has witnessed you in the act of committing murder? He will have as close a hold on you as you on him. You will be tied together for the rest of your miserable lives. Each of you will serve a life sentence, as surely as

if you were tried and found guilty. Of course, you may prefer it to the gallows. If I were Berringer I should live in
dread of Pounceforth's brittle nerves, and if I were Pounceforth I could not sleep at night knowing what Berringer
is capable of. Still, it was a hard choice to make, Pounceforth."

"I did not know I had made it," Pounceforth said in a
whisper.

"You have made it," Berringer said. "I would not take
the gun now if you offered it to me. Is it licensed, Pounceforth? How are you going to dispose of it? Have you
thought these things out? It requires intelligence to kill
without fear of discovery."

"Your first murder was discovered," Pounceforth said in
a voice thick with hatred. "I discovered it."

"By chance, purely by chance. I will not pretend I have
covered my tracks perfectly, but I have not done badly."

"Not until now," Hilary said; he had felt the pressure of
the gun through his clothing lessen and knew that there
was still a slender chance of his survival. "I am not the
only one who knows that there is a link between you and
Pounceforth. I have told Honeychurch and Kate Cardew.
If Miles dies tonight, if I disappear, Honeychurch will tell
the police all I have told him. You will be questioned and
there are two of you; sooner or later you will give the
wrong answer, Pounceforth, when you begin to be afraid
of the consequences. Sooner or later Berringer will let his
respect for his own powers trick him into being too clever.
One lie too many or one too few and you will both be
done for."

"Let that thought be your consolation," Berringer said.
Hilary saw that he, too, was trembling. He judged the moment auspicious for an attempt to save himself and

shouted suddenly, "Turn the gun on him, Pounceforth! Shoot him and get away. I will swear it was to save me you did it."

Pounceforth's hold wavered; Hilary gripped his wrist and forced it round and up. Three shots rang out; three bullets described invisible swift curves towards and away from the indifferent sky. Berringer turned and crashed away through the undergrowth, bellowing strangely.

"He is frightened," Hilary said in wonder, "and about time, too. I was beginning to think fear was something only I could feel."

"I am not frightened!" Pounceforth said desperately and wrenched himself free. "There are three bullets left and no more time to talk——" His arm rose; Hilary shut his eyes; a startling sound rang in his ears, but it was not a shot. He opened his eyes and saw the gun lying on the mosaic ten yards away. He also saw Berringer arrested in his flight at the far edge of the pavement and turning back towards them.

"Do it yourself!" Pounceforth sobbed on the edge of the wood. "Do it yourself, Berringer. I have had as much as I can stand!"

Hilary caught his arm again and pushed him into the shadows. "Why the hell did you do that? Your life is worth no more than mine once he gets the gun."

"You get it," Pounceforth wept. "I have given you a chance."

"What do you take me for? I am no hero. I am going to run, Pounceforth, and so are you, if you have any sense."

Berringer's shoes tapped over the mosaic. Pounceforth drew himself out of Hilary's grasp and began to run towards his discarded weapon. Hilary saw that the man was out of his mind, but it was too late to stop him. He was within a few feet of Berringer when Berringer picked up the gun and fired. Pounceforth fell with a gentle scream but continued to move, pulling himself upon his hands and knees.

Hilary yelled, "Berringer! Have you forgotten the ten uniformed policemen?"

Berringer uttered a wild cry and turned the gun towards Hilary; but one of the ten uniformed policemen raised and lowered his truncheon with precision, and the arm that held the gun was broken, and the gun lay once again on the mosaic, as did Pounceforth.

"You underestimated my conversational powers, gentlemen," Hilary said.

ENVOI

Berringer was no better a shot than Pounceforth after all: his bullet had traversed some unimportant muscles in Pounceforth's leg, and his last victim had strength and sense enough to turn Queen's evidence. The body of his first was discovered in less than an hour on Pounceforth's directions; after that, Inspector Burnivel spent many months gathering statements and correlating scraps of evidence. Eventually there was a case against Berringer that no jury could have resisted. A little later the editors of several important publications were faced with some difficulty in composing an obituary; there could be no doubt that Berringer's death was a loss to his profession and to his patients, but there was some reason to suppose that his continued existence might have resulted in other and more regrettable losses.

"It is a good thing that I don't have to write a mourning notice," Hilary said; he had been given at least temporarily the editorship of the *Journal*. "Jubilation would not be suitable, and I don't think I could grieve with any conviction. It's an ill wind, as he himself once remarked."

"And the cloud has a silver lining," Roberts remarked to Honeychurch. "Even a golden one, for Latimer at least. I have discovered a trust fund administered by the Royal College of Surgeons which is to be used for just the sort of research Latimer proposes. They will give him the money and he can stay here to do the work."

"I wish I could forget it all," Kate said to Miles a few days after their marriage. "It is a terrible thing to bear grudges against the dead, and I do try not to; but I can't forgive Berringer for what he did to you. I don't hate Pounceforth so much: he did so little, comparatively."

"Of course we shan't forget it," Miles said, touching her hair with a wondering movement of his hand. "It didn't even bring us together; we were together already."

"And might have been parted."

They drew closer together.

"Do you know when I most thought we would part?" he said suddenly. "It was later than you think: it was when I began to get better and they told me what Hilary had done. I knew then I ought to let you go, to give you the chance to choose again. I thought you might have mistaken pity for love; it is a mistake other people have made and repented. But when it came to the point I hadn't the courage. Pity is not such a bad substitute as people make out."

She shook her head. "It was never pity. I am so glad you didn't have the courage. You are good enough for me as you are: I don't know that I could bear it if you were quite perfect."

They kissed; they were perfectly suited to each other.

"Will nothing ever cure you," Inspector Burnivel said peevishly to Honeychurch, "of this idiotic belief that a few well-meaning amateurs can deal with a criminal?"

"We had no facts to offer you," Honeychurch said in a pacifying tone, "and you attach so much importance to facts. It is all right now. You have seen Pounceforth's anonymous letters and the girl's body and the skeleton and

Mr. Trimble's order book and Berringer's toupee. It is easy for you, in the light of Pounceforth's admissions."

"If Pounceforth had stuck to the anonymous letters, everyone but the poor girl would still be alive," Burnivel remarked, giving to the epithet "poor" a curious explicitness. "That skeleton was an error of tactics. It takes my powers to trace an anonymous letter, but Berringer could trace the skeleton through Mr. Murivance: it was bad luck for the old gentleman that he knew Pounceforth himself and knew of Throckleford. He had to die. Then Latimer linked Berringer to Mr. Murivance and to Throckleford with that book; so he had to die too."

"And Pounceforth only remained alive by a fortunate chance."

"And Dr. Scott."

Honeychurch said mildly, "In Scott's case one might name a dispensation of Providence. He had every right to stay alive. I am not so sure about Pounceforth."

In late April, Prentice was moved to take a few days' holiday while Matheson spring-cleaned the museum. On his return he found the skeleton standing once more near the door.

"I didn't know what to do with her, sir," Matheson explained.

"She cannot be allowed to clutter up our space forever. We will see what Professor Honeychurch thinks."

But Honeychurch said, "So far as she belongs to anyone, she belongs to Pounceforth. And Pounceforth has gone away and left no forwarding address."

"She is out of place here," Prentice remarked.

"If I might be permitted to make a suggestion, sir——"

"Of course, Matheson."

"If nobody else wants her, I would give her a home."

"You do not mind having a memento mori?" Honeychurch said in some wonder.

"Well, no, sir. It is things one keeps forgetting that one dislikes being reminded of, I find. In my calling it wouldn't do to be upset by dead things. And it would be more likely to remind me of Mr. Murivance. It would be a sort of tribute to his memory."

Honeychurch and Prentice looked at each other, and Honeychurch nodded. "Take her, Matheson. Take her by all means. No one will quarrel with the fitness of your sentiments."

"I believe he would have liked me to have her, sir."

"Of course he would," Hilary said. And added in awe and admiration, "For Matheson is a man who could make even a skeleton happy."

ABOUT THE AUTHOR

Edward Candy is a successful writer living in England. He is the author of eight novels. *Bones of Contention* is his first novel for the Crime Club.